An outstanding and unexpect‗ ... *...‗y and its*
metaphysical counterpart. Ver‗

Edward Gunzig, Professor of C...‗ology in the Department of Theoretical
Physics at the Free University of Brussels

*This attempt to bring together physics and the philosophical vision of
the cosmos in a coherent whole is interesting and worthwhile.*

David Bohm, Professor of Theoretical Physics at Birkbeck College, London
and author of *Wholeness and the Implicate Order.*

*I am an unashamed reductionalist and as such I regard holism as
mysticism.*

Stephen Hawking, Lucasian Professor of Mathematics at Cambridge
University and author of *A Brief History of Time.*

*Holistic concepts have a profound role in modern mathematics and
physics, and need not be mystical; Hagger's broad sweep over the
holistic scene is not so constrained by scientific desiderata.*

Roger Penrose, Rouse-Ball Professor of Mathematics at
Oxford University and author of *The Emperor's New Mind*

*Sums up the rise and dominance of reductivism to date admirably.
Drawn together like this, the story is startling: it will surely look so at
some future time. Challenging, serious and timely.*

Mary Midgley, Philosopher and author of
Science as Salvation, A Modern Myth and its Meaning.

*It is nearly 100 years since William James first warned against the
reductionism which he saw increasing in the scientific and philosophic
spirit of his day, the 'but only' element as he labelled it. Even he would
have been dismayed at the extent of the empire the element has
established in all the disciplines he valued, and how much he would
have supported all those who value the quality and range of a truly
comprehensive modern awareness as Nicholas Hagger does in all he
has written with a rare intellectual passion in all his work since* The
Fire and the Stones.

Sir Laurens van der Post

THE UNIVERSE AND THE LIGHT

Nicholas Hagger was born in 1939 and educated at Chigwell School, Essex, and Worcester College, Oxford. During the 1960s he lectured at overseas universities in Iraq, Japan (where he was a Professor) and Libya. During his time in the Middle and Far East he visited many cultures and civilisations and absorbed their religions, art, literature, philosophy and history. He was the first Westerner to discover the Cultural Revolution in China in March 1966, and he was an eye-witness of the Gaddafi Revolution in Libya in September 1969. During the 1970s he lived in London and wrote for *The Times* and other newspapers, taught and pursued his research into world history and a world vision, metaphysical poetry, science and philosophy. His "Grand Unified Theory" of world history and religion, *The Fire and the Stones,* appeared in 1991, together with his *Selected Poems: A Metaphysical's Way of Fire,* which covers 30 years of his poetic output. At home in many disciplines, he divides his time between Essex and Cornwall where he balances the active life of an educationalist, rediscoverer of lost knowledge, interpreter of current affairs and synthesiser of approaches to the universe with the contemplative life of a philosopher, poet, mystic and man of letters.

By the same author

The Fire and the Stones

Selected Poems (1960–1990)
A Metaphysical's Way of Fire

The Universe
and the Light

*A New View of
the Universe and Reality
and of
Science and Philosophy*

Essays on the Philosophy of Universalism
and the Metaphysical Revolution

NICHOLAS HAGGER

ELEMENT

Shaftesbury, Dorset ● Rockport, Massachusetts
Brisbane, Queensland

Published in Great Britain in 1993 by
Element Books Limited
Longmead, Shaftesbury, Dorset

Published in the USA in 1993 by
Element, Inc.
42 Broadway, Rockport MA 01966

Published in Australia in 1993 by
Element Books Limited for
Jacaranda Wiley Limited
33 Park Road, Milton, Brisbane 4064

Cover design by Max Fairbrother
Cover illustration *Galaxy* by Imtek Imagineering
courtesy the Telegraph Colour Library
Printed and bound in Great Britain by
Dotesios Ltd, Trowbridge, Wiltshire

British Library Cataloguing in Publication
Data available

Library of Congress Cataloging in Publication
Data available

ISBN 1–85230–404–9 (Hardback)
ISBN 1–85230–413–8 (Paperback)

CONTENTS

INTRODUCTION

These three essays were written independently and where they overlap they complement one another.

The first one is a fuller version of *Illumination and Metaphysics: A Grand Unified Theory of the Mystic Light in History, Nature and Cosmology*, the opening lecture I gave to 450 scientists at the 1992 Scientific and Medical Network's Mystics and Scientists conference at Winchester. The second one was written to introduce Universalism as the metaphysical antithesis of reductionism and to explain the thinking behind my centre at Epping (the Foundation of the Light), which is opening many people to the Light. The third one was written as a paper for a Symposium on Reductionism's Primacy in the Natural Sciences, which was held at Jesus College, Cambridge in early September 1992. The paper was circulated among fifteen speakers who included ten Professors of Physics, Biology, Physiology, Neurology, Astronomy and Philosophy in Britain and the U.S.A.

Taken together the three essays provide an introduction to my thinking. The first covers the theoretical framework, how the Fire or Light unifies all disciplines and triggers a Metaphysical Revolution in each. The second covers the practical side, explaining how Universalism is creating a global network of inter-religious groups which are bringing down the Light. The third deals with the movement against reductionism in philosophy and science, and sees metaphysical Universalism as an extension of physicalist holism and as creating a new metaphysical science which has launched the Metaphysical Revolution.

The penultimate paragraph of *The Fire and the Stones* says: "A new 'Fire of the World Movement' would devise a new Universalist terminology and would have three aims, which would correspond to the three levels on which we said at the outset the Tradition of the Fire can be read: to bring individuals to an existential confrontation with the

vi

Fire; to bring to pass a Metaphysical revival within all societies, cultures and civilisations, but particularly within the European and North American civilisations, so that university syllabuses contain metaphysical as well as secular texts; and to show that the Fire is the common ground for all civilisations, whose central idea it is, that the Fire provides the common ground for the coming world-wide culture, and that it is an impetus for world peace. It is time to establish a Foundation - a Foundation of the Light - which will further these aims and safeguard the Metaphysical Revolution."

The Foundation of the Light was created in May 1992 and it thus has three planks to its platform: at the personal, practical level it encourages people to see the divine Light, which is the way of mysticism and involves a Mystic Revival; at the theoretical level it promotes a Metaphysical Revolution in all disciplines, which involves the academies or universities; and at the universal level it promotes Universalism, the essence of all religions, a philosophy that has replaced Existentialism and involves the arts and all religions.

This book follows this pattern. The first essay covers the mystic Light and the Metaphysical Revolution. The second essay covers Universalism and amplifies the themes in the first essay. The third essay focuses on the Metaphysical Revolution in philosophy and science, and amplifies themes in the previous two essays. The Universalist history theory, touched upon in the first essay, is presented in embryo in Appendix 1, and it may be useful to grasp it as a whole there before plunging into the detail of *The Fire and the Stones*. Appendix 2 and Appendix 3 flesh out the metaphysical view of the origin and creation of the universe, and of evolution and brain-function.

All the main themes of the new movement in mysticism and metaphysics, known as Universalism, are here. The history theory shows that the rise of Universalism is linked to the rise of the North American civilisation (as its heresy) and to the decline of the European civilisation (as an expression of the coming conglomerate's cosmopolitanism): to stage 17 of the American civilisation and stage 44 of the European civilisation. Universalism is ahead for both the North American and European civilisations. In this respect I am a historicist in believing that historical events reveal the motive forces of culture as photons reveal waves of light; in asserting that historical events are governed by the laws of the freely chosen stages I have outlined in *The Fire and the Stones*; and in affirming that movements in the soul and cultural phenomena express themselves at certain times, in certain stages, and are therefore determined by history, i.e. by the laws that underlie and bring in these freely chosen stages.

Nicholas Hagger
September 1992

THE NATURE OF LIGHT: ILLUMINATION AND A METAPHYSICAL THEORY OF EVERYTHING

(A new reunification of knowledge in terms of the One Fire or Light)

Today many, especially in the younger generation, are searching for something, and I sometimes think of Omar Khayyam's words in Fitzgerald's translation:

"Myself when young did eagerly frequent
Doctor and Saint, and heard great argument
About it and about: but evermore
Came out by the same door as in I went."

In other words, "I heard the lecture but it didn't change anything; I searched but never found anything." There *is* something to find, and those of us who are engaged in the Metaphysical Revolution and Mystic Revival see an urgent need to speak directly and openly to all who are searching about the fundamental and crucially important mystic Light, which is hinted at in so many texts but which never features centrally.

The mystic Light is the metaphysical reality behind the universe and Nature, and as scientists - particularly cosmologists - are probing the universe and coming up with discoveries like Smoot and Mather's ripple effect, it is vital that scientists should be aware of the significance of the mystic Light, and reconsider the presuppositions of the traditional scientific world view. These are that the scientist is separate from the universe he describes with physical sense data and experimental measurements, or after the relativity and quantum theories with mathematics. Some progressive scientists (including two Scientific and Medical Network research groups) have already questioned these presuppositions and have suggested extensions and

1

revisions that include a more intuitive and spiritual approach to reality; and they are in the process of concluding that the non-logical, mystical apprehension of a metaphysical reality can no longer be ignored by the current scientific world view. As one who has known it fully for over 20 years and who sees its importance to cultures and to history and the universe from territory T.S. Eliot occupied between poetry and cultural history, I propose to offer a broad perspective on the mystic Light and present a unified vision. My theme is an exciting one: the metaphysical or spiritual Light behind history, Nature and cosmology and how the metaphysical vision offers a Grand Unified Theory of everything - how the Light is central to mysticism, religion and history, permeates Nature (including consciousness) and cosmology, and offers a unified model of the universe that denies the solely materialistic outlook: a unified vision that has created a new movement.

What is the experience of this Light? You know it when you are ready by entering within yourself and moving behind your rational, social ego into your soul, your universal being, in contemplation, closing your eyes and letting the Light come through. What you see may look like a painting, *Emerging*, by an American artist, Marilyn Sunderland. Or like the dome of Il Gèsu, Rome painted by Baciccia[1] which shows Christ as Light. St Augustine described his experience in 400 AD:

"I entered within myself. I saw with the eye of my soul, about (or beyond) my mind, the Light Unchangeable. It was not the common light of day.... What I saw was something quite, quite different from any light we know on earth. It shone above my mind.... It was above me (or higher), because it was itself the Light that made me, and I was below (or lower) because I was made by it. All who know the truth know this Light, and all who know this Light know eternity."

St. Hildegard of Bingen saw the Light in the course of her spiritual awakening c1140: "When I was forty-two years and seven months old, a fiery light (or burning light) of tremendous brightness coming from heaven poured into my entire mind. Like a flame that does not burn but enkindles, it influenced my entire heart and my entire breast, just like the sun that warms an object with its rays."

Hildegard in fact knew this Light all her life and she confirms St Augustine's view of it:

"These visions which I saw, I beheld neither in sleep, nor in dream, nor in madness, nor with the eyes of the body..., I perceived them in open view and according to the will of God.... From my infancy up to the present time, I now being more than seventy years of age, I have always seen this light, in my spirit (or soul, Jung's translation) and not with external eyes, nor with any thoughts of my heart, nor with the help from my senses.... The light which I see is not located, but yet is more brilliant than the sun,... and I name it 'the cloud of the living light'.... But sometimes I behold within this light another light which I name 'the living light itself'. And when I look upon it every sadness and pain vanishes from my memory, so that I am again a simple maid and not as an old woman." Hildegard died in 1179AD.

Let us be quite clear, according to the many eye-witness accounts of it, the Light the mystics Augustine and Hildegard saw is not just an inner psychological phenomenon, it has an independent existence from human beings. It comes from the beyond, beyond the physical sense data, experimental measurements and mathematics on which the current scientific world view is based. Look at Hildegard's own painting[2] of her spiritual awakening c1140. The Fire or Light comes from outside her head into her soul. The painting makes this very clear. Energy from the beyond enters and enlightens the body and illumines the soul. Look at the sculpture of St Teresa of Avila by Bernini.[3] Again, the Light comes from outside St Teresa. The effect of this Light from the beyond is to light the soul like a candle, as you can see from the halo round Christ in a 6th century icon from St Catherine's monastery, Sinai,[4] and from the halo round the Indian Vallabha.[5] In the course of doing this it enlightens the body as you can see from paintings of Mohammed.[6] Note, enlightenment is of the body or the aura, illumination of the soul and mind.

In this experience, the Light is not an image or a symbol or metaphor, but a reality, an actual state of consciousness. The soul is actually filled with an outside Light, which is a universal energy from the beyond, not an image that can be consciously visualised at will as happens in American Actualism. Rather as in Zen Buddhism, the seeker sits and waits in a silence beyond language - the unconscious - and the Light comes to him, shining in his soul, like the sun coming out of cloud and shining in a puddle. "Our attainment of enlightenment," says a Zen authority, "is something like the reflection of the moon in water. The moon does not get wet..... The whole moon and the whole sky find room enough in a single dewdrop.... Just as a dewdrop or drop of water offers no resistance to the moon in heaven, so man offers no obstacle to the full penetration of enlightenment."

According to the evidence in *The Fire and the Stones*, the vision of the Fire or Light has widely been interpreted as the vision of God. The vision has been described by mystics in varying phrases, all to do with Fire or Light. I do not want to repeat the documentation, but it can be found in Appendix 3 of that book. St. Augustine, who saw the Light as "the Light that made me", also, saw it as God: "But what do I love when I love my God?... It is true that I love a *light* of a certain kind....What is that Light whose gentle beams now and again strike through to my heart, causing me to shudder in awe yet firing me with their warmth? I shudder to feel how different I am from it, I am aglow with its fire. It is the Light of Wisdom." "God is my sweetness and my Light", "God is the intelligible Light." In the western mystical tradition of St Augustine, Pope Gregory the Great and St Bernard, God is (to quote Blake) "Light".

Now there is a tradition that goes back to Dionysius the Areopagite, c500, and beyond him to St Gregory of Nyssa, an eastern tradition that God is a Darkness behind the Light.

Dionysius, writing in Greek, advocated a turning away from the world of the senses for an ecstatic union with the "light from the divine darkness" which is God. God is "veiled in the dazzling obscurity of the Secret Silence" and is unknowable, the "Darkness of Unknowing". (Compare our *Cloud of Unknowing*.) To Dionysius, God is defined in negatives: not this, not that. This eastern tradition regards light as imagery, God as beyond all imagery. It is possible with Meister Eckhart to distinguish God from the Godhead, the transcendent Godhead (the origin of things which does not act) being dark and the immanent God being Light. Today this position is held by Bede Griffiths, the Catholic monk who has lived in India since 1955, for whom the Godhead is transcendent darkness and beyond all symbolism and diversity.

I do not want to get into speculations about the *source* of the vision of God or the Absolute, about the exact point at which transcendence becomes immanence, whether God or the Godhead is Light or the Darkness behind or within the Light. I believe the Light does not constitute imagery as it is from the beyond, and that it is the manifestation of an immanent God to the human soul. Or as John the Beloved put it, "God is Light and in him is no darkness at all" and "the Light shineth in the darkness". I want to focus on the reception of the Light in consciousness, using Husserl's phenomenology to "bracket out" the source and focus on consciousness. Phenomenology studies consciousness by bracketing out or eliminating the object of consciousness, and in the same way it can study the Light in consciousness by bracketing out the Light and focusing on consciousness, which is where Dionysius the Areopagite received the Light: "our intellect (intellectus means perception, not reason) is united to the superlucent rays, being illumined thence." If you focus on the reception of the Light in consciousness, on the experiences Augustine and Hildegard and many others describe, there is broad agreement that the Light is *from* God.

The nature of this Light which is received in consciousness, then, is, according to the tradition, divine. It is either God or from God, an attribute of God, and it is spiritual. It is quite different from natural or physical light. In Part One of *The Fire and the Stones* there are hundreds of eye-witness accounts of the Light, evidential reports on inner experiences, and I have looked at 5,000 years of experiences and interpretations of the Light and drawn together all the best known recorded instances from all cultures, and I conclude that experiences of the Light have been interpreted as direct perceptions of God, or revelations from God which are "beneath" God, the One source of the universe which is a reflection or manifestation of this source, who is a Fire or Void or spiritual sun, who sends a divinising spark or influx of Light into the soul which transforms or converts the ego by making the heart burn and by giving Eternal Life.

The Light is central to mysticism. In her book *Mysticism*, Evelyn Underhill regarded this spiritual Light as being central to the Mystic Way, which progresses from awakening to purgation, a Dark Night of the Senses, to illumination, thence to ecstasy and contemplation, and a Dark Night of the Spirit, and thence to the unitive life. This journey involves a centre shift from the lower human mind of the rational, social ego to the soul, the new higher divine centre's universal being, and the Light from the beyond is received in the new centre's silence beyond language. (My transformational poem, *The Silence*, is about this centre shift.) The centre shift and experience of illumination only come at the right time, when the seeker is ready. It does not happen before a seeker has reached his mid-20s. (In a chart in his American classic first published in 1900, *Cosmic Consciousness*, Bucke lists 43 illumined people and their age at illumination. The great majority are over 30.) Reality manifests downwards, and a seeker has to withdraw from all the debris in the human ego to the higher level of the soul, in order to receive it. The centre shift can safely be effected with guidance, which in the West the Church used to provide and all too often now does not.

The mystic Light brings benefits to those who make the transformational shift from their rational, social ego to their soul or universal being. The Light facilitates the shift by detaching people from their senses, taking them beyond attachment and desire, and the peace and inner serenity that follow are perceived by them as being of great benefit. For as they start living at a deeper level of consciousness, their senses are cleansed and purified, with startling abruptness they lose their desire to smoke or drink alchohol and in some cases cease to be promiscuous. To see the Light (the vision of God) is not a sign of madness or a symptom of schizophrenia or some such medical condition, and it cannot be put down to fatigue or stress, though fatigue or stress can precede it and provide a useful onslaught on the social ego which hinders its reception as in the case of Pascal. On the contrary, the Light solves psychological problems. Jung said in his commentary to the *Secret of the Golden Flower*, after quoting Hildegard's, "I have always seen a light in my soul": "As a rule, the phenomenon is spontaneous, coming and going on its own initiative. Its effect is astonishing in that it almost always brings about a solution of psychic complications, and thereby frees the inner personality from emotional and intellectual entanglements, creating thus a unity of being which is universally felt as 'liberation'."

As a result of their gnosis, the illumined receive infused wisdom, divinely revealed knowledge. Hildegard says that after her first experience of the "fiery light": "All of a sudden I was able to taste of the understanding of the narration of books. I saw the psalter clearly and the evangelists and other Catholic books of the Old and New Testaments." In due course those who know the mystic Light in their soul or universal being have a deep sense of the unity of the universe and are filled with a sense of its meaning and purpose. It is sometimes said that mysticism is self-regarding and a waste of time, but in fact while it unites the soul with all the universe the Light fills the soul with the

7

desire to help others, to found new institutions for others so that love can be expressed for all in a practical way. The illumined become naturally good and increasingly divinised, as they live through a divine part of themselves. They are gentle and kind to all creation, and live at peace, valuing their environment. They are motivated, curious about everything, want to learn and to make a unified statement. Their lives are lived with a deep inner aim that is daily in view, and they found institutions like St Teresa's convents. Those who return from the near death experience speak of going into a tunnel at the end of which is the brilliant Light, and on their return they turn to love, have a thirst for knowledge and lose their fear of death.

The following are just some of those who have known the Light: Patanjali, Zoroaster, the Buddha, Mahavira, Lao-Tze, Jesus, St Paul, St Clement of Alexandria, Plotinus, Mani, Cassian, St Augustine, Pope Gregory the Great, Mohammed, Bayazid, Al-Hallaj, Omar Khayyam, Suhrawardi, Hafez, Symeon the New Theologian, Hildegard of Bingen, Mechtild of Magdeburg, Moses de Léon, Dante, Angela of Foligno, Meister Eckhart, Tauler, Suso, Ruysbroeck, Kempis, Rolle, Hilton, Julian of Norwich, St Catherine of Siena, St Catherine of Genoa, St Gregory Palamas, Padmasambhava, Sankara, Guru Nanak, Hui-neng, Eisai, Dogen, Michelangelo, St Teresa of Avila, St John of the Cross, Boehme, Herbert, Vaughan, Crashaw, Traherne, Norris, Law, Cromwell, Marvell, Milton, Bunyan, Fox, Penn, Naylor, Mme Acarie, Baker, Pascal, St Francis of Sales, Mme Guyon, Wesley, Blake, Swedenborg, Shelley, Emerson, Tennyson, Browning, Arnold, Newman, Mme Blavatsky, Trine, Jung, T.S. Eliot - and a host of others who enshrine the best of Western and Eastern culture.

This Fire or Light has been well known throughout the world's cultures and is the central idea in all the religions of both East and West; for example, it has manifested in the Christian and Orthodox transfiguration and Hindu Yogic samadhi, Mahayana sunyata and the Void of Tao, Buddhist enlightenment and Zen satori. The vision of the Fire or Light expresses itself in a religion and inspires "stones" (temples, cathedrals and mosques). Religions are the inspirers of civilisations.

*

We should now turn to history. The Light which is central to mysticism and religion is also central to history and to the rise and fall of civilisations. Gibbon, Spengler and Toynbee have all tried to account for the rise and fall of civilisations. Gibbon saw the Roman civilisation falling as a result of barbarians and the advent of Christianity; Spengler saw the West as declining from old age, its soul power becoming intellectual. i.e. rational; and Toynbee saw civilisations rise and fall in terms of challenges responded to or not responded to by their leaders.

The central point of *The Fire and the Stones* is that history is not a random flux of events. Civilisations grow through a vision of the Fire or Light (such as the one Mohammed saw in his cave) which creates a new religion round which an empire gathers, and they decline when the Fire is absent. The vision of the sacred Fire or Light, which is also the vision of God the mystics (and poets and artists) have seen, inspires and is the central idea of the 25 civilisations of history, and the renewal of the Fire or Light each generation by contemplative mystics causes the civilisations and their "stones" to rise and be renewed, while failure to renew the Fire results in their decline and hastens their fall.

The book charts the historical relationship of religions and civilisations, and proposes a theoretical basis for their rise and fall. Each of the 25 civilisations grows when the vision of the Fire or Light or God is strong and vitalises its religion - the Fire is channelled into the society of each civilisation through its religion - and each civilisation declines when the vision of the Fire weakens, and turns secular. In relation to the public domain, the Fire or Light then becomes a lost knowledge, as has happened in Europe.

9

(It was well known in Europe in the 17th century - the Metaphysical poets are full of it and there are references in Tennyson, Browning and Arnold - but after 1880 there are only fleeting references in Eliot and Yeats and one or two other established European poets, such as Eliot's "The fire and the rose are one.") Each civilisation passes through 61 precisely dated stages, and goes through a rise-and-fall parabola resembling a rainbow. The stages of all 25 civilisations are freely chosen but appear inevitable; they are parallel, like the fractals of Chaos Theory. To confine a wealth of evidence and detail within one volume I tabulated the stages in *The Fire and the Stones*, and they are summarised in a chart, which shows the coming stages of living civilisations. When a civilisation reaches stage 61 it passes into another civilisation.That is the broad sweep of my view of history.

There is not space now to go through all the implications of the patterns, but it is important to grasp that one of the ingredients of the definition of a civilisation as opposed to a culture is that each civilisation has its own religion and its own distinctive god. I must assume an aquaintance with the 61 stages, which are detailed in *The Fire and the Stones*, and I confine myself now to some lessons that can be drawn from the chart. First, the Fire or Light is central to civilisations - not generals, economists or politicians (not Schwarzkopf, Thatcherism or Marxism, or American or Russian Presidents or European Prime Ministers). Secondly, Gibbon and Toynbee were wrong about the Byzantine culture; it was not a part of the Roman civilisation (Gibbon) and did not lead to the later Ottoman civilisation (Toynbee), but developed into the Byzantine-Russian (Orthodox) civilisation, stage 43 of which was the Communist stage. Using that time scale in *The Fire and the Stones*, I was able to predict the end of Communism and the U.S.S.R., which I associated with Yeltsin. Thirdly, America has a world role ahead. Paul Kennedy is wrong in seeing a decline ahead of America in *The Rise and Fall of the Great Powers*. The neo-Hegelian Fukuyama is right to see American liberal democracy as being prevalent from now on but he is wrong to think it will permanently be so. The prevalence is just an aspect of a stage.

Fourthly, the European civilisation is about to enter a United States of Europe in stage 43. The difference between stage 43 and stage 46 - union and federalism - explains why Europe is entering a union but Russia is coming out of one.

Within this pattern, notice there is a heresy which becomes orthodoxy when a new people take over. There is a link between stage 17 and 44 of different civilisations. In America the heresy that is growing began embryonically with the 18th century Universalism of de Benneville, Murray and Ballou (see page 133). In our time it has become associated with the New Age; this is changing, and the fully developed heresy will become the orthodoxy. It can be called "Universalism" in the sense that it focuses on the universal, common Fire or Light in all civilisations' religions. It is the Universalist view that all religions are one religion based on the Fire or Light.

I should add in passing that stage 39 of civilisations, scepticism, is a natural consequence of the weakening of the central idea of a religion and civilisation which happens at the breakdown of certainties. The scepticism we experience today is a natural symptom of the stage in European civilisation we have reached. The renewal of the civilisation's central idea in the course of a cosmopolitan conglomerate brings a corresponding movement away from scepticism to Universalism.

The Fire began in Central Asia, passed to the Indo-Europeans, and then spread from culture to culture and civilisation to civilisation until the present time. If the Fire was present in one area at a certain time, then it can be presumed that it was known about at another place at a later time. This is a diffusionist view, but not in terms of trade as William McNeill saw history in *The Rise of the West*. Rather the Fire, not trade, inspires civilisations by moving from place to place from before c5000BC to the present and will inspire a new world-wide civilisation. I see this as a stage of a young existing civilisation (the North American civilisation) rather than as a new civilisation. All civilisations will eventually flow into one, for a while. The Fire or Light is the common ground for all cultures and so the unity of all cultures rests on the Fire - as, eventually, does world peace. Man evolves within civilisations which transmit values from generation to generation (for example, Fra Angelico hands on the Christian vision to the painters who succeeded him in our European civilisation) and man as a whole evolves through the work of individual contemplative mystics within specific civilisations. So contemplative mystics are the heroes of history.

The Fire and the Stones offers a Grand Unified Theory of world history and religion in terms of this vision of the metaphysical Fire, a view that history has purpose through the working out of the vision in civilisations. The patterns of the rising and falling civilisations, and the supporting archaeological evidence, are there if the vision of the divine Fire is accepted as the central idea of civilisations. It may be argued that any idea could produce similar patterns, but my book finds that civilisations formed round a credible vision of the divine, which is most often stated as Fire or Light. Certainly if you make economists or generals (homo economicus or homo militarius) central to history rather than contemplative mystics (homo illuminatus) then the patterns cease to be there; the patterns are only there if civilisations grow round a central metaphysical vision which eventually turns secular. Toynbee at one point admitted defeat in his search for *his* central idea, the cause of the genesis of civilisations: "I have been searching for the positive factor which within the last five thousand years, has shaken part of Mankind...into the 'differentiation of civilisations'.... These manoeuvres have ended, one after another, in my drawing a blank". He did not know it, but he was looking in vain for the Fire or Light. (Toynbee was aware of the need for a civilisation to undergo a spiritual regeneration, but he never associated this with the mystic

Fire or Light.) The vision of the Fire or Light unlocks the patterns and enables history to be seen in a new way.

My view of history accords with the perspective of quantum physics. Quantum physics tell us that light is both particles and waves, and history, too, is both particle-like events (such as battles) and waves of civilisations lasting thousands of years. In *The Fire and the Stones* I show the process of the waves (of light or quanta), which can only be known in relation to the metaphysical Fire. The stages of civilisations are like superstrings in physics which string together human events which are the building blocks, the fermions and bosons.

Tracing the mystic Light in history solves historical problems and perhaps creates a new subject. If biophysics is concerned with the solution of biological problems in terms of the concepts of physics, then histo-metaphysics is concerned with the solution of historical problems in terms of the concepts of the mystic-religious vision of metaphysics and in terms of quantum theory. We might call it "quantum history" or "quantised history" instead, or "process history"; history which operates through waves of metaphysical light which are quanta, packets of visions of individual contemplative mystics and strings (or superstrings) of events, and which lose strength as they cross thousands of years of time just as waves of gamma photons or quanta released in remoter intergalactic space lose strength as they cross space and end up as microwaves.

*

We now need to widen our view of the Light to include Nature and cosmology, and focus on the combination of the spiritual Light, the consciousness which receives it, and the natural, physical world, including natural light. The Romantic poets saw Nature as one Spirit. Wordsworth, for example, in *The Prelude* appeals in 1798/9 to the:
  "Wisdom and Spirit of the universe!

Thou Soul that art the eternity of thought,
That givest to forms and images a breath
And everlasting motion, not in vain...
...didst thou intertwine for me
The passions that build up our human soul."
Wordsworth says that as a result:
"An auxiliar light
Came from my mind, which on the setting sun
Bestowed new splendour."
Shelley in *Hymn to Intellectual Beauty* and *Mont Blanc*
refers to the Spirit in Nature as "the awful shadow of some
unseen Power" which "floats though unseen among us",
and as "the everlasting universe of things" which "flows
through the mind". Both saw Nature as a unity, a whole, in
terms of this "Spirit" and "Power". Significantly in *Science
and the Modern World* (1925) Whitehead picks out
Wordsworth and Shelley as reacting against the materialism
of 18th century science: "Berkeley, Wordsworth, Shelley
are representative of the intuitive refusal seriously to accept
the abstract materialism of science." Whitehead's
philosophy of organism saw Nature as one, unbifurcated or
undivided between mechanism and the vital world of human
beings, in *Process and Reality*, which was subtitled *An
Essay in Cosmology* (1929). In other words observer and
observed, knower and known, consciousness and the
physical world are part of the same reality, which is one
organism. Or as David Bohm has expressed it in *Wholeness
and the Implicate Order*, drawing on quantum theory in a
way many modern physicists do not accept, one wholeness
with an implicate order.

In fact we can now see that this one Nature is the product
of a quantum vacuum which is as large as this universe and
present around the book you are holding. The Brussels
school associated with the Belgian physicist, Edgard
Gunzig, has pioneered work on how virtual particles escape
the quantum vacuum and become real particles if they are
combined with energy, and therefore how a universe can
come out of the quantum vacuum (so there is something out

14

of nothing). These virtual particles definitely exist, and are the building blocks of Nature: building blocks of matter (fermions, i.e. electrons, protons and neutrons) and building blocks of consciousness (bosons, i.e. photons and virtual photons, neutral z particles, + or - w particles, gluons and gravitons if they exist). The idea that the building blocks of consciousness can emerge from the quantum vacuum makes many physicists uneasy, and physicists have been wary of mathematical explanations which interpret quantum mechanics in a way that includes mind and consciousness. Bohm has said that the implicate order which underlies matter is matter rather than mental consciousness.

However, it is my view that the metaphysical Fire or Light permeates the quantum vacuum, bringing everything that is into existence and ordering it as Wordsworth's "Spirit" and Shelley's "Power" within Nature, and that consciousness, organisms and matter unfold, as Bohm has suggested, from the implicate order of a less than random quantum vacuum. This brings us to the whole question of order within the quantum vacuum, and hidden variables. In quantum theory, randomness or indeterminacy is fundamental and identical electrons in identical experiments behave with apparent randomness, and many physicists assert that all nuclei were originally in an identical state, and that one nucleus decays and another does not on a random basis. Einstein did not accept the randomness ("God does not play dice with the universe"), and he proposed a presently unknown property, referred to as a hidden variable, which causes one nucleus to decay and not another, and spent the rest of his life looking for it. It has not been found but that does not mean it does not exist, despite the 1982 Aspect experiment. Bohm's theory is also constructed on hidden variables, and as today physicists base theory on what can be observed and measured experimentally, they reject the idea of hidden variables that cannot be measured, of a reality in the microworld, and so Bohm's dissenting view of order within the chaos has not been accepted by many physicists. However, as an inveterate intuitive extender of what can be observed and measured experimentally, and a defender of a reality in the microworld, I propose that the metaphysical Fire or Light in the quantum vacuum is itself the unknown property, the controlling, ordering hidden variability which determines which nuclei decay and which do not, and explains the apparent indeterminacy or uncertainty the 24 year old Heisenberg saw in terms that give order to randomness. The uncertainties in electron behaviour need to be analysed in terms of the effects of the metaphysical Light in the microworld, and of the relative intensities of its high frequency waves. Science needs to devise the means to gather this observational evidence, and the coming Large Hadron Collider may be of help here.[7] (Compare the Greeks' atomistic viewpoint which could not be tested until recently.) According to this view, the Fire or Light gives out orderly matter and consciousness.

The Fire in the void of the quantum vacuum, then, pours particles into creation. To put it another way, the Fire or Light behind Nature disgorges photons of consciousness and particles of living and non-living matter, which are in effect "bits of light" as photons outnumber matter-building particles by many millions to one and are absorbed by them. (It is interesting that Bohm has described matter as "frozen light"). Light constitutes a larger part of reality than is generally realised. In the universe as a whole there are many millions of photons for every matter-forming elementary particle, especially in space, which is full of photons that have been travelling for thousands of millions of years without coming close enough to matter to be absorbed.

The oneness of Nature and consciousness which have emerged from a quantum vacuum that is itself within the metaphysical Fire or Light includes consciousness's interaction with the electromagnetic spectrum of physics. Visible or natural light is electromagnetic radiation whose composite effect can be detected with the human eye - we can't see individual rays - and it is both electromagnetic waves and streams of particles, photons or light quanta (particle-like packets of light energy), which travel in straight or slightly curved lines from the sun and space. Practically all the natural light at the surface of the earth comes from the sun, either direct or reflected by the moon, clouds or other objects. The blue sky light is sunlight that has changed its direction during its journey through the atmosphere. The energy radiated by the sun originates in its interior. Under this high temperature (10-20 million degrees) matter is transformed into energy when protons (nuclei of hydrogen atoms) react with one another to form alpha particles (nuclei of helium atoms) and positively charged beta particles (positrons or positive electrons). The energy released is partly heat but most of it is radiation of a very short wave-length, photons called gamma rays. The energy of each gamma photon is a million times greater that of a photon of light. These gamma photons force their way to the surface of the sun and divide into less energetic photons, and by the time they have reached the surface of the sun visible light has resulted. Each original gamma photon is now 1,000 smaller photons.

Let us be more specific about natural, visible light. It exists independently of matter. When it is not influenced by matter it travels along a straight line. From this it has been concluded that light is a stream of particles called photons or light quanta (particle-like packets of light energy). But sometimes light behaves in a way reminiscent of waves on a water surface or rather of a crime wave, and so light is sometimes called a wave motion. In space light has an electromagnetic wave motion, which consists of an alternation between electric and magnetic fields. A ray consists of a series of short-lived electric and magnetic fields. When a wave of light penetrates matter, which is composed of charged particles (positive atomic nuclei and negative electrons), it influences matter with forces from the electric and magnetic fields. The human body is built like a sieve, to allow light energy to pass through it, energising it on the way. Light is sometimes particles, sometimes waves - a dualistic phenomenon. This dualistic aspect of light, and the dualistic nature of physical reality, appear contradictory to common sense but that should be regarded as a deficiency in common sense and its mental ability to visualise complex reality.

We can measure the wave-length of light in monometres (millimicrons), micrometres (microns), millimetres, metres and kilometres or specify frequency (oscillations or waves per second), and the shorter the wave-length the higher the frequency. Visible light is a tiny portion of what we receive. On the long wave-length, low frequency side we find invisible infra-red, radio and television waves and microwaves. On the short wave-length, high frequency side we find invisible ultra-violet, X-rays and gamma rays. Radiation that filled the universe from shortly after the Big Bang - cosmic background radiation - began as X-rays and gamma-rays, but as space has stretched since then (through inflation) the energy is now microwave with wave-lengths around 1 millimetre.

Our consciousness (i.e. our conscious and unconscious mind) is itself a spectrum within Nature's sea of energies and radiations and vibratory frequencies, only a tiny portion of which can be perceived by the senses. According to a very modern view which Gary Zukav reflects in *The Seat of the Soul*, in a chapter entitled *Light*, consciousness is a spectrum with bands in which light energy is received and experienced at differing frequencies. This light energy includes natural light, and manifested spiritual Light which the non-finite, high frequency part of ourselves can receive, and also the healing energy and various paranormal energies. Our consciousness, then, is a system of light, a spectrum that is part dense (low frequency), part spiritual (high frequency). When we shift the *level* of our consciousness we shift the frequency of our light - allow high frequency currents of energy to run through us and we experience an increase in our energy. When we shift the *centre* of our consciousness from our social ego to our universal being we live among higher frequency currents of energy than before. To put it another way, we are both particles and waves of light. In our social ego we are particles, and in our universal ego or essence we are waves - just as history is events and wave-like patterns.

So the electromagnetic spectrum is also a diagram of our consciousness. Our brain waves are in the region of 10 cycles per second (beta and alpha from 30 to 8, theta and delta from 8 to 0.5). Our consciousness is surrounded by invisible rays of higher frequency all the time - they're around us now, gamma rays and radio waves and invisible rays of natural light - but we can begin to pick them up consciously when we shut down our own beta and alpha interference and go into radio silence at 4 cycles per second (meditation and higher consciousness), and open to all the invisible higher frequency cosmic and metaphysical rays of the spectrum. Then we are filled with high frequency invisible rays which energise us, including rays of the Light from the gamma end of the spectrum. We have to open from the densest part of ourselves to the less dense universal being in the huge non-physical Light area above the frequency range in which most humans exist. Unlike the physical, which is measurable, the metaphysical is unmeasurable (although its effects may be measurable), but when it enters consciousness in the universal being, I suggest that it is *received* at a point on the spectrum, in the region of 4 cycles per second. The brain physiologist Peter Fenwick has called for "a new science of consciousness" and I propose this substantially new view as a contribution to such a new science, that in universal being, consciousness receives and is filled with the energies of the entire spectrum.

Healing energy can be understood in terms of this consciousness spectrum. It can be placed at the gamma end along with the Light. Of the healing energy of the Light, Agnes Sanford writes in *The Healing Light*: "In the course of our experiments we have come to the conclusion that a vibration of very, very high intensity and an extremely fine wave-length, with tremendous healing power, caused by spiritual forces operating through the mind of man, is the next thing science expects to discover." She adds that patients don't feel the high energy, only the effect of the high energy which feels like heat. (Compare visible light, we don't see the individual rays but see their composite effect). The shorter the wave-length the higher the frequency and the greater is the energy of every photon. In the *reception* of healing, molecules with low energy receive and absorb photons of high energy (channelled from the healer), and become more energetic or excited. In Nature this process leads to photochemical reactions and photosynthesis, a process by which green plants and organisms receive and absorb light energy and transform it into chemical energy. (Some bacteria, including those found 20 miles underground, obtain their energy from inorganic substances such as sulphur in volcanic springs and as they also require oxygen, most of which is formed through plant photosynthesis, they indirectly profit from light energy.) Visible, natural light produces similar reactions in bodies, and both causes and heals diseases, and spiritual Light, which may contain ideas or love or awareness of meaning, excites less energetic photons of consciousness. In the *giving* of healing, the process of course is the other way round: photons of high energy (in the healer) are transformed into lower energy in a process that seems to be associated with bioluminescence, the active radiation of light by living creatures such as glowworms and fireflies. The emission of photons (or biophotons) from a living creature requires the collection of a large amount of energy in molecules which is then passed from a high energy level to a lower one as chemical energy is converted to radiant energy. This seems to be what happens when healers channel high spiritual energy (the Light) and pass it out to their lower energy patients - and when mystics are filled with the Light, which William James called "photism" and which causes consciousness to glow like bioluminescence and emit biophotons like a glowworm.

THE NATURE OF LIGHT

In my view, then, the visible, natural light of Nature and manifested non-physical Light of consciousness seem to be within a continuum of energy and frequencies. Just as the frequencies of infra-red, ultraviolet and microwave light coexist with the visible light band but are undetectable by our physical senses, so frequency ranges of the manifestations of non-physical Light co-exist with visible light but are likewise undetectable by our physical senses. If we make the centre shift from the 5 sensory personality of the social ego to the multisensory /multidimensional/ paranormal energy of the universal being we become more radiant and energetic, and see Nature with the unitive mystical vision as a spectrum of metaphysical-physical Light.

*

Cosmology also benefits from being understood in relation to the Fire or Light. Cosmology brings together the natural sciences, particularly astronomy and physics, to understand the physical universe as a unified whole, how it began and how it will end. The vastness of the physical universe of cosmology is awe-inspiring, and can rapidly be conveyed in a few images. Look at a nebula of hydrogen gas 6,500 light years away. Within it is one of the most massive stars known, an immense ball of stars, 47 Tucanae on the edge of our galaxy, 13,000 light years from us; it has 100,000 stars brighter than our sun. Then look at our galaxy with its fried egg shape. And then, having got it in perspective, look at earth seen from the moon. In the 20th century, cosmological science has been out there among these billions of stars and has applied mathematical reasoning to ground traditionally occupied by a branch of metaphysics (cosmology), but it has been unable to find the unification in which all physical interactions are explained by one (simple and beautiful) set of equations, and it has been unable to provide definitive answers to the questions about the origin and structure of the universe.

THE UNIVERSE AND THE LIGHT

Following the First Scientific Revolution of Galileo and Newton, and the Second Scientific Revolution of Einstein, relativity, quantum mechanics and post-war subatomic physics (particle physics); in the 1980s there has been a Third Scientific Revolution in cosmology that has joined together quantum theory and relativity, the microcosmic and the macrocosmic, the subatomic and the cosmological, to show how our universe manifested from the quantum vacuum. This really began in 1973 when Stephen Hawking, courageously battling with his crippling disease established in formulae that black holes emit particles and evaporate. In 1980 Hawking proclaimed that by the year 2000 there would be a consistent (materialistic) unified theory in which all physical terrestrial interactions are described by one set of mathematical equations: particles, fields of force, quantum theory, general relativity, black holes and the beginning of space-time, the origin of the universe - and gravity. In 1980 Hawking was excited about a quantum gravity theory called supergravity. By the mid-1980s, he changed his view and backed the string theory, that tiny strings vibrate and interact; superstrings which according to the equations only work in 26 dimensions. (4 we know about, 22 are hidden.) "Quantum tunnelling" is a more recent idea. (In December 1991 Dr. Jonathan Halliwell, a former student of Hawking's, claimed in *Scientific American* that "quantum tunnelling" offers a "universe without a cause", and "no creator is required".) In 1988 Hawking spoke of "if" (not "when") we discover a complete theory, and now no-one expects it before 2010 at the earliest.

We are not near a Grand Unified Theory of physics. Of the four forces physicists are trying to unify, the weak and electromagnetic forces have definitely been unified. An attempt has been made to integrate these with the strong force. The unification of these three forces works theoretically but there is no indication that it works in practice. There have been tests for the last five or six years, and in all those tests no one event has given any evidence that the theoretical unification is any more than a possibility in quantum terms. So what about gravity, which holds the universe together, including our galaxy? It seems logical that gravity should be quantised as the other three forces are (at least theoretically) and that there should be gravitons which are emitted or absorbed in gravitational interactions, but there is no proof. Physicists like DeWitt have been working on this for a long time and have drawn a blank, and we're left with a materialistic notion that real nothing became a quantum vacuum (a sea of cosmic energy) by quantum processes involving virtual potentialities of being in this emptiness, and then a universe (by virtual particles becoming real particles).

At this point it is necessary to say something about Hawking (who is regarded by many as the leader of the Third Scientific Revolution) because he has had a great influence on many people, having been in the top ten hardback best-seller list for over 184 weeks. What he is doing is clearly wonderful, but despite his outstanding mathematics and his heroic fight against ALS - and I want to say it gently - Hawking is perpetrating a sceptical materialism which asserts that matter gives rise to mind. Hawking believes that mathematics (which is just a language) offers the key to understanding the universe, and his reality is a materialistic one of particles and black holes. Hawking has described the universe of Eastern mysticism (Hinduism, Buddhism and Taoism) as an illusion, and he claims that there is no room for God the creator, and he speaks of the finding of a unified view of physics as the "ultimate triumph of human reason" (i.e. the rational, social ego) " - for then we would know the mind of God". Many would say that Hawking can never reduce God to materialistic, rational mathematical terms because when our reason (as opposed to our universal being) approaches the Absolute it can only see it in terms of its own limitations because our reason is finite and the quantum vacuum behind the larger universe is infinite. There is another view of cosmology, the view of the mathematics-using Paul Davies who has championed a paradigm shift from materialism and mechanism in *The Matter Myth* and in *The Mind of God*. In March 1991, Bohm told me, "I think the universe is infinite, a local event within an infinite whole. There is something real behind physics. They will never find a (materialistic) Grand Unified Theory in physics." And John Barrow seems to be saying the same in *Theories of Everything* (that materialistic theories of everything are far from sufficient). John Barrow ends his book *Theories of Everything*: "There is no formula that can deliver all truth, all harmony, all simplicity. No Theory of Everything can ever provide total insight." Which I understand to be unoptimistic about the prospects of materialistic Theory of Everything.

The truth is, Grand Unified Theories are only possible if they include metaphysics - as Einstein said, "anyone who studies physics long enough is inevitably led to metaphysics" - and we can never understand phenomenal reality - Nature - in terms of particles and fields alone. In his book Hawking asks, "What is it that breathes fire into the equations and makes a universe for them to describe?" Notice he uses the word "Fire". And the answer we have given is just that, the metaphysical Fire or Light which has widely been regarded as God.

This Fire or Light makes possible a metaphysical rather than a materialistic Theory of Everything within cosmology. It is likely that the unifying principle that explains everything and provides a theory of everything will have simplicity and beauty, and will unify relativity, quantum theory and gravity and explain historical patterns and trends, string-like chains of particle-like events. I have already argued in my Grand Unified Theory of world history and religion that the presence or absence of the vision of the Fire in history provides a context which explains historical patterns and trends, that religious Fire inspires civilisations, entering the electromagnetic spectrum of a consciousness which is Light. Is it not possible that the wave-like metaphysical Fire or Light orders, organises and controls all known and unknown waves of energy, including natural light? That it is the vital energy that holds all four physical forces in place as a fifth force, activates the potentialities in the quantum vacuum and is behind the excitation and inflation that led to our universe of matter and hidden variables? According to the tradition, in its transcendent form the Fire or Light was present before the beginning of time, before there was any universe. It was behind the quantum vacuum and became immanent within it. I suggest this Absolute influence from another dimension is crucial to the unification which the physicists are still seeking in Nature, that spiritual Light may turn out to be the missing ingredient, a fifth force, in providing a full metaphysical Theory of Everything. Newton, in his later metaphysical alchemistic period, attempted to find an expanding force in the universe to counteract gravity, an expanding force he associated with light. (My *Cambridge Ode Against Materialism* is about this; see the Metaphysical Commentary at the end.) Could a quantised and spiritual version of Newton's expanding force, an expanding metaphysical Fire or Light, unite gravity and the other three forces and govern hidden variables and inflation? This is a lovely idea.

If the Fire pervades the universe and all that can be known, then it can set matter dancing and images whirling in minds, it manifests into creation from a hidden, implicate order as Bohm has suggested, organises cellular division and breathes through our lungs, moves the seas and grows all trees. In which case, mystics *see* the organising principle of the cosmos. The time is right for a new metaphysics of Light, just as the Gothic time was right for Grosseteste to form a metaphysics of Light in the 13th century.

*

I am now in the metaphysical aspect of my theme of the Light behind history, nature and cosmology. Metaphysics is the study of what is or Being, or Reality, its meaning and structure.

In *Global Mind Change* Willis Harman distinguishes three kinds of metaphysical perspectives: materialistic monism (the belief that matter gives rise to mind, i.e. scientific materialism); dualism (matter plus mind, i.e. the Cartesian position of Sir John Eccles); and what he calls transcendental monism (the belief that mind gives rise to diverse matter). Transcendental monism sees the ultimate stuff of the universe as consciousness, an Idealist view that is similar to that of the perennial wisdom. On this view mind or consciousness is primary, and matter-energy arises in some sense out of mind. Many scientists have today come to the view that this third metaphysic fits best with 20th century discoveries.

To this I would add a fourth perspective: metaphysical non-duality (the belief that a metaphysical Reality gives rise to both matter and mind, that a unity gives rise to a diversity). On this view, the Fire or Light that permeates the quantum vacuum unfolds consciousness as well as Nature from a metaphysical source outside the physical world. Monism has no diversity, but non-duality implies both a unity at the transcendent metaphysical level and a diversity at the immanent, physical level.

Traditionally metaphysics used reason and logic to approach the structure of Reality, but philosophers (including the Scientific and Medical Network's Metaphysical Research Group) recommend extensions and revisions of the current scientific and philosophical world view to include an intuitive and mystical apprehension of reality.

A metaphysical view of Nature (or science) regards metaphysics as a branch of philosophy; and as a study of the transcendent or supersensible, of the reality that is "beyond or behind the physical". We are interested in both meanings. As a branch of philosophy metaphysics traditionally comprises ontology (the study of Supreme Being or Being or Reality), which is related to theology;

epistemology or psychology (what can be known about Being); and philosophical cosmology (the structure of the universe). If we do not interpret ontology in a purely materialistic sense to mean the phenomenal world, and if we split the psychology into transpersonal or spiritual psychology - after Edith Schnapper's *The Spiral Path of Spiritual Psychology* and Zukav's *The Seat of the Soul* - and human or humanistic psychology, then we get the following fourfold scheme for a metaphysics with four subdivisions that covers a fourfold manifestation process according to the tradition:

> Ontology - the study of Being or Reality within Nothing, Supreme Being or transcendent Godhead/ immanent God as the latent Fire or Light which can be experienced mystically, One, Light containing truth and wisdom, theology;

> Transpersonal psychology or spiritual psychology - quantum vacuum, symbols and collective unconscious (through which Jung linked the mind to the beyond) received in universal being, Non-Being permeated in its transcendental form with the potentially immanent Fire or Light or God manifesting into immanence, potentialities of Being and Becoming (virtual particles);

> Human psychology and epistemology - soul and consciousness in terms of human psychology, self-reports of subjective, inner experience (inner knowing) as well as sense data, the reception of the Fire or Light in consciousness, the vision of the central idea of civilisations in history, Being and Becoming, potentialities of Existence;

> Cosmology - the structure of the universe according to Einstein and Bohm, Nature, matter, natural light

or lux, astrophysics, space exploration, Becoming, Existence.

In my view this Fire or Light, Heracleitus's "ever-living fire" (fragment 30), undergoes a fourfold process of manifestation which is reflected in the four subdivisions of metaphysics. First it is present latently and transcendentally in real nothing which existed transcendentally before the beginning. Secondly, it is immanent within Non-Being, the Void or quantum vacuum which contains all the potentialities of being, and which is present now in this room. Thirdly, it is therefore immanent within Being, which came into "being" immediately the beginning took place 15 billion years or so ago and is present in Becoming, in the subatomic particles of physics, and which contains all the potentialities of Existence, the "virtual particles" or "virtual photons" from the quantum vacuum, and what in biology Rupert Sheldrake has called "morphogenetic germs". Being is the unity behind Existence or Becoming. Fourthly, in Existence it partially manifests into form as Nature and, the photons of physical light and all the different existents in creation, the phenomenal world of cosmology. Existentialism regards this world of existents as the only world. (I follow this scheme in my poems).

For those who know the Kabbalah, this fourfold scheme reflects the four worlds (divine, spiritual, psychological, physical) of the Kabbalah. For mystics, the One non-finite, transcendent Light becomes immanent and can be *experienced*, so metaphysics ceases to be rational as it was for Leibniz and Kant, and becomes existential, in the sense that the Being of the One can be experienced. This is a new *existential* Metaphysics or Metaphysical Existentialism (which I prefer to call Universalism as Existentialism is dead and gone and is waiting to be replaced by a post-Existentialism). We are living in a sea of Light, and for mystics the One is known in illumination in the silence of the quantum void/eternity, where symbols and archetypes and Ideas and Platonic Forms break into being.

THE NATURE OF LIGHT

As the Romantics and Whitehead saw, the universe is not a dead, materialistic one. It is filled with thought which flows into the soul and guides people together, providentially arranging their lives so their choices are guided as they move from attachment to lower self to unattached, desire-free universal being in accordance with the workings of a universal Law (that God, the Fire or Light, works in our lives). The Light guides and nourishes with understanding, wisdom and thought. The universe is not one of "benign indifference" (Camus's *L'Etranger*), the feeling of the sceptical, rational ego, but an active one that pours love through our universal being, as the sea pours through a sponge.

The idea that the universe is a giant thought (Sir James Jeans) rather than a giant machine has won support from physicists such as Jack Sarfatti, one of the physicists who to the disgust of some physicists have sought to link quantum mechanics and mind. Sarfatti (in 1975) envisaged a "great cosmic brain that permeates all parts of space", adding: "I suspect that general relativity and quantum theory are simply two complementary aspects of a deeper theory that will involve a kind of cosmic consciousness as the key concept" - our Fire or Light (which Bucke referred to in his famous book of the title as "cosmic consciousness"), and which acts as a Universal Mind. This cosmic consciousness is, perhaps, a cosmic brain of Light (or information-processing system, Wheeler), which manifests into form so that the whole universe is a thought which thinks us and thinks all forms into existence, and that is present everywhere. Bohm has said, "Light can carry information about the entire universe"[8], information which can include love, understanding, compassion and healing, and which can perhaps move at superluminal speed (faster than the speed of light, which, according to conventional scientific doctrine, cannot be exceeded). When superluminary particles - photons - move at speeds greater than light, time slows down and distance is shortened and the two ends of a light ray have no time between them and no distance, and there is immediate contact. Quantum nonlocality. The superluminal information transfer theory may be in physics what Jung's synchronicity is in psychology, and it may explain how the metaphysical Light travels vast distances instantaneously, pouring truth and wisdom into consciousness, and information into matter at speed which can exceed the speed of light. (It is possible that natural, visible light is used as a vehicle for the information-carrying, and that we are programmed from the cosmos via light which enters our physical eyes and activates the pineal gland.[9])

The metaphysical Reality is hidden behind the world of appearances and phenomena which conceals it, just as the Chinese characters "Chin Hua", "Golden Flower", conceal a central character "Kuang", "Light". There was a time in the 9th century AD when it was heretical to speak of the Light in China, and so the character for "Light" was hidden between two characters "Golden Flower". The One hidden behind Nature has been shown in art. Look at the swirling Fire-like energies in *Starry Night* by van Gogh. Look at the rays of Light in the *Mystic Lamb* by van Eyck. Look at the rays from the Aton that came down to the 12th century BC Akhenaton and Nefertiti[10] in Egypt, and notice the rays of light have healing hands. Look at the paintings of the Milanese artist, Fleur Beverley; for example, *Dove*, *Structures* and *Reflections in Time*.

Such a metaphysical view of Nature and cosmology that reinstates the Fire or Light behind all involves a critique of the assumptions of modern science, some of which can be labelled objectivist, positivist and reductionist. Traditional pre-1900 science makes an objectivist ontological assumption of separateness between the observer and objective reality and a positivist epistemological assumption that physical sense data and measurements are the sole evidence on which the scientific picture of reality is to be based, and that we can understand a whole by studying its parts or particles (reductionism). In fact, in the 20th century, science has split: the relativity theory put an end to such separate thinking - the observer is inextricable from what is being observed; Whitehead's philosophy of organism reunites man and Nature in terms of a reality beyond positivism; and the quantum theory and non-local theory have demonstrated that particles cannot be separated from the whole, that we are inseparable from it like fish in the sea; while a new epistemological assumption has held that the scientific picture of reality should be based on mathematics, not physical sense data alone. The traditional sceptical view has been contradicted by non-traditional and holistic scientists who believe they can understand the universe through mathematics. But, as we have seen with Hawking, the non-traditional scientists have not been able to grasp the hidden reality behind Nature, and a more intuitive approach than mathematics claims scientists' attention.

Now a new metaphysical science (in whose preparatory work Willis Harman is prominent) - an answer to Bergson's call for a "much-desired union of science and metaphysics" - makes a unified ontological assumption that the universal energies of the Fire or Light work within the wholeness of observer and observed, man and nature, mind and matter, parts and the whole to explore the order behind the uncertainty principle of 1927, and an intuitive epistemological assumption that consensual self-reports of subjective, intuitive inner experience of the Fire or Light are equally as valid as physical sense data, measurements and mathematics. Metaphysical science thus makes an alternative set of metaphysical assumptions for science.

This metaphysical science has declared a Metaphysical Revolution which focuses on the Fire or Light, which in turn has restored the metaphysical vision, and it connects with a movement of metaphysical renewal in a number of disciplines and the arts. This movement began in the 1980s after 300 years of Humanism, Scepticism and Materialism which have dominated our perception of all academic subjects and which see man as merely body and mind. Our revival of the Fire or Light, the ontological Reality within

31

the infinite universe, as an existential (or rather, post-existential) experience (as opposed to rational speculation) establishes a new view of man and the universe, in which both are permeated by influxes of the metaphysical Fire, and connect in the universal being. It is this new view of man and the universe in terms of the Fire or Light that makes possible the Metaphysical Revolution. I declared this Metaphysical Revolution in April 1991, chanting some lines from Shelley's *Ode to the West Wind*, "Scatter, as from an unextinguished hearth/Ashes and sparks, my words among mankind!"

The Metaphysical Revolution is moving into all disciplines. It challenges and absorbs the sceptical, materialistic vision into the physical layer of its fourfold scheme. In philosophy, it challenges and absorbs logical empiricism and linguistic analysis. No longer can the philosopher sit in his armchair and quibble about meanings - American spacecraft are flying round the planets and sending back data which is transforming our cosmology. The universe is back in place of language. Twentieth century sceptics, humanists and materialists who applied their scepticism, and language, to all transcendental experience of the beyond, and the logical positivists and linguistic analysts of the Vienna Circle, who set up the verification principle to see all inner experience as unverifiable and therefore outside philosophy, have dismissed the inner reality of the Light in terms of the linguistic social ego, and most recently Derrida (who was refused and then awarded an Honorary Degree at Cambridge in 1992) has written in this tradition, and deconstruction and post-structuralism follow it, asserting that there is no reality outside language ("il n'y a rien hors du texte"). However, the universal or transcendental being which is entered in the silence of contemplation can see inner reality from the "I" behind Descartes' "I think therefore I am", and empirical philosophers like Derrida trespass when they cross over into the contemplative territory of the universal being from the rational, social ego and assert with their reason that there is no reality outside language that can be known in contemplation. The reason is a useful tool - I am using it now - but where appropriate reason should be informed by the beyond. The Metaphysical Revolution's epistemological assumptions now include the assertion that the intuitive experience of the mystic Light in universal being has validity in philosophy along with sense data, experimental measurements and mathematics, and it has declared a revolution against logical positivism, holding with Whitehead that "the purpose of philosophy is to rationalize mysticism." In fact I have co-ordinated plans to publish a book of essays by different thinkers on the Metaphysical Revolution in philosophy.

The Metaphysical Revolution progresses under the banner of Universalism, for it focuses on the universal being where the universal energies of the Fire and Light flow from the universe with great universality, where the spiritual and divine enter the soul. Look at the meditator in Serailian's painting[11], which captures the essence of the Universalist vision. At the individual level it defines man in relation to a universal vital energy, the Fire or Light, the vision of God which is seen in the divine part of ourselves. At the social level, Universalism sees this universal energy as central to all societies, cultures and civilisations (as we've seen in our consideration of history). At the global level Universalism proclaims that the vision of this universal energy of the Fire or Light is the common ground for a universal world-wide civilisation and religion, for all people's experience of the Fire or Light is ultimately the same, regardless of where they live. Look at a painting in Hildegard's *Scivias*[12] (the sixth vision of the First Part) in which all beings celebrate creation. This painting of Hildegard's shows Hildegard's unity in terms of the Light. At the cosmic level Universalism presents the non-finite, non-material part of our consciousness, universal being.

Universalism is the new Romanticism (its forerunner). Just as Romanticism passed into all the arts between the late 1790s and 1830, so Universalism is set to expand from the

1990s. It is a post-Existentialist movement. It holds that "essence precedes existence" (to turn the Existentialist phrase), (i.e. emphasising the universal being or essence which can penetrate through the phenomenal veil into Being, rather than emphasising the phenomenal world of existence). It is a movement in philosophy and the arts, and in history and physics and cosmology and other disciplines. In all these, Universalism sees man in the universe in terms of the universal energies which flow into his universal being, not just in terms of his social ego. Universalism's consequences will be profound (as were Romanticism's consequences). There will be Universalist painting, music and literature with Universalist equivalents of Constable and Turner, Beethoven and Brahms, Wordsworth and Shelley. To take poetry, for example,the poet ceases to be a marginal figure: true metaphysical poetry reflects the truth of the Fire or Light as it did in the 17th century, and as the vision of the Fire or Light is the central idea of civilisations, the poet who writes of the Fire or Light renews his civilisation's central idea, and must be central to his civilisation. And so it is with painting and the other arts. There are plans to introduce Universalism in a London production which will feature all the arts.

Universalism also has a religious dimension. Already groups of ten or twelve are forming, directed to communing with the Light which is beyond. Some are studying *The Fire and the Stones*. Collectively they form a network - a new Mystic Revival in the West. Some are doing this in conjunction with a particular religion. Many are outside all religions and collectively they potentially form a new Universalist religion. The Foundation of the Light covers two Foundations at my centre in Epping (which doubles up as a school I founded in 1989) - the Universalist Foundation, which will promote Universalism in the arts, and the World Metaphysical Foundation of the Light, which will work for a world Metaphysical Revival with the Fire or Light as the potential common ground for all cultures.

THE NATURE OF LIGHT

Rediscovering the lost knowledge of the Fire or Light, the Universalist Metaphysical Revolution offers a unified model of the universe and of knowledge. The One is immanent in our quantum universe, and unites mysticism, religion, history, philosophy, biology, physics, cosmology and much else in terms of the metaphysical Light which illumines the soul and fills it with love, wisdom and truth. Our unification of mysticism, history, Nature and cosmology has laid the foundations for a reunification of knowledge in terms of the Fire or Light. *The Fire and the Stones* has done the hard part: reconciling the vision of the Fire or Light in mysticism and religion with world history. This is a Grand Unified Theory: in physics, the equivalent of unifying   three of the four forces. It stops short of a Theory of Everything, the equivalent of unifying all four known forces. The initial evidence for a total reunification of mysticism, religion, history, philosophy, biology, physics and cosmology involves assembling a new combination of mystics' eye-witness accounts and historical, quantum and spectrum data, to reveal the workings of the metaphysical Fire or Light; and questioning all randomness in history, science and philosophy - the view of history as a random flux without a pattern, the scientific materialism of Hawking, the uncertainty principle of Heisenberg, the logical linguisitic empiricism of Derrida - in terms of a teleological vision of meaning, pattern and order which is known intuitively by our universal being. Science should then   devise new means of gathering observational or experimental or mathematical evidence on the workings - the effects - of the Light, following up this intuitional insight. The science of the Fire or Light is in the same stage now that the atom was in the time of the Greeks. A Theory of Everything in terms of the Fire or Light for the first time incorporates a unified field theory of consciousness and matter, the quantum vacuum and the electro-magnetic spectrum, and holds that tides from a sea of photons pour into our consciousness, which receives impressions of visible objects through natural light, and of the invisible through the spiritual Light.

So in conclusion, what do we now understand by the "Nature of Light"? The Light is of divine origin and is spiritual. It emanates from the Godhead, permeates the quantum vacuum and the universe and is received in the universal part of consciousness, the non-material universal being, as the vision of God. It is behind Nature, which is frozen Light, and as the mystic illuminative vision it is the central idea of history. At the same time it manifests downwards, through the fourfold metaphysical process of manifestation, into a spectrum that includes natural light.

If the vision of the Light is the central idea of civilisations, and of poetry, and of mysticism and lies behind physics; then the urgent necessity is to lead people to an experience of illumination, to make it experiential rather than cerebral. This will only happen when they are ready, but to this end we need to revive the function of the mystery schools and temples of the East and of times past. The Foundation of the Light aims to do this, and holds mystery school meditations to this end.

In closing, I want to emphasise the importance of focusing now on this metaphysical Light. There is a Zen saying, "Show a fool the moon, and he looks at your finger." I have shown the moon. It is not my finger that is important, but gnosis of the moon, the Light which provides a unified model of the universe and of knowledge.

Notes

1. See plate 47 in *The Fire and the Stones*.
2. The self-portrait or "Protestificatio" which introduces *Scivias*, plate 31 in *The Fire and the Stones*.
3. See plate 46 in *The Fire and the Stones*.
4. See plate 44 in *The Fire and the Stones*.
5. See plate 42 in *The Fire and the Stones*.
6. See plate 102 in *The Fire and the Stones*.
7. See page 66 for further details.
8. Ed. Renée Weber, *Scientists and Sages*, p48.

9. This view can be found in Jacob Liberman's *Light, Medicine of the Future*, pp 29-31. Liberman observes that the pineal gland assists us in bonding with the universe.
10. See plate 13 of *The Fire and the Stones*.
11. See plate 89 in *The Fire and the Stones*.
12. See plate 48 in *The Fire and the Stones*.

WHAT IS UNIVERSALISM?

The term "Universalism" has been used of religion and history. In religion it originally included the belief that all mankind's souls can eventually be saved, and it has therefore come to involve a concern with the souls of every human being outside all religions. In history, it suggests a concern with all mankind, and therefore with every civilisation.

The new philosophy of Universalism, which is beginning to find its way into all disciplines and the arts, has a different meaning. It posits a new view of man in relation to a new view of the universe. It holds that man can open to the universal energy of the Fire or Light, which is in the universe and comes into the universal being or soul with great universality. Universalism sees both man and the universe in terms of the Fire or Light, and its most important perception is that man lives in a two-way relationship with a universe of Light. Universalism is a new optimistic philosophy of man's place in the universe and of the human condition in relation to the Fire or Light. It has both theoretical and practical aspects, and is the true antithesis of philosophical and scientific reductionism, rather than holism. Universalism includes a metaphysical level whereas holism has more to do with the physicalist whole in space and the secular world of physics than with the metaphysical reality of the manifesting Light.

The shades of meaning contained in the word "Universalism" include: (1) "universal", suggesting an energy which is applicable to all persons in the world; (2) "universe" or all existing things, the whole creation, suggesting an energy that permeates all things; (3) "universal being", suggesting the soul which all people of all nationalities have; (4) "universality" which is common to all mankind, suggesting an experience (of illumination) which is common to all mankind; (5) "universalist religion" or religion concerning every human being in mankind, suggesting a religion that promotes the Light in the soul of every human being, a religion in which all religions are one; and (6) "universalist history" or history concerning every human being in mankind, suggesting history in which the vision of the Fire or Light is central to all civilisations.[1]

In its new, layered sense of the word, "Universalism" is thus about much more than religion and history. It includes mysticism and cosmology (in the first two shades of meaning).

*

The new view of man of Universalism comes from man's own knowledge of his place in the universe, of his response to the mystical One Light. But Universalism is not just mysticism, although it draws heavily on the Mystic Way. Universalism differs from mysticism in that whereas mysticism involves passing through some five or six stages on the Mystic Way (of which more later) and Light is only really involved in the third (illuminative) stage and the fifth (unitive) stage, Universalism relates to the permanent presence of the Light as the vision of an immanent God which is the central idea of each civilisation and is always "there" to come in; and it safely takes seekers into its presence to familiarise them with what is ahead, even though they are not yet ready to open to it.

Universalism does not regard illumination as a happening that may or may not occur in the course of the Mystic Way. Rather it regards the Light as the raison d'être of the Mystic Way, the climax of the first mystic life and the foundation of the second mystic life, and it approaches the Light on a regular basis, waiting patiently for it, and does not leave its advent to chance. Moreover, whereas mysticism generally finds expression in connection with a particular religion (e.g. Christianity, Islam), Universalism focuses on the soul's individual and particular experience of the Light, regardless of any particular religion.

WHAT IS UNIVERSALISM?

Universalism approaches the Light and its properties through the inner, contemplative eye. In the 13th century St Bonaventure wrote that man has three eyes[2]: the "eye of the flesh" which is the bodily eye that perceives sense data; the "eye of reason" which understands concepts of philosophy and processes and interprets sense data; and the "eye of contemplation", which perceives and understands Truth and the Light. Universalism emphasises not the empiricist eye of the flesh or the rationalist eye of reason, but the contemplative eye of contemplation. In contemplation, when he is meditating, man knows the "living Light" (Hildegard) which contains properties of healing, wisdom, understanding and love; a vital energy which can guide and transform consciousness and bodies.

Universalism relates the contemplative eye to the structure of consciousness. It sees man's consciousness as a system of Light on a spectrum (see p18), and believes that when he channels and conducts energy of a high frequency level (the Light) then his consciousness is transformed from a dense, low frequency level.

Universalism sees consciousness as being non-materialistic in relation to the brain. It shares a growing feeling among scientists that the photons of consciousness are not dependent on the brain, that they operate above it and use it. Consciousness can be explained in terms of the quantum vacuum, as David Bohm first suggested 40 years ago. On this view a ground state of consciousness is subject to excitations - our thought processes - which work when excited photons give rise to a "Bose-Einstein condensate" (in which parts not only behave as a whole but *become* a whole). This accounts for our alpha, beta, theta and delta brain waves. The firings of individual neurones in the quantum vacuum-like ground state are bound together by the coherence of a Bose-Einstein condensate and the resulting patterns can be seen on an EEG: beta waves from conceptual thought, alpha for relaxed wakefulness, theta for dreaming sleep and delta in dreamless sleep. Quantum processes do seem to be at work in consciousness, in the interconnection of all portions of the brain. According to Evan Harris Walker of the NASA Electronics Research Centre, Cambridge, Massachussetts, "Consciousness is a nonphysical but real quantity" and the process involved in the interconnection of all portions of the brain is not chemical or electro-chemical but may still be particle-related and due to "quantum mechanical tunnelling".

Universalism's connection between consciousness and the Light makes possible a new view of man which takes its inspiration from the time before scientific materialism suffocated science and philosophy with mechanism, and which draws on some of the anti-materialistic movements of the last 300 years. In the 17th century the Christian vision of the Light was still proclaimed from pulpits throughout Europe, and the Metaphysical poets were full of it. During the rational Augustan 18th century the vision began to fail, and the Light vision passed into German Idealism and Romanticism, and eventually (much more faintly) into Modernism and Existentialism. Each of these movements failed for different reasons, and Universalism, in reconnecting with the essence of the 17th century in Europe, draws on their attempts to continue the tradition of the Light through a different view of man. Nevertheless the new view of man of Universalism differs in emphasis from that of its forerunners: Idealism; the German rational approach to metaphysics; Romanticism; Modernism; and Existentialism.

The Universalist view of man does not emphasise that the world or reality is essentially ideas or mind or consciousness or spirit, as does traditional Idealism; it sees both consciousness or mind and matter as emerging from, and in contact with, the metaphysical Reality of the Fire or Light. Metaphysical Idealism draws on Plato, Plotinus, Spinoza and Leibniz and is directly opposed to materialism, realism, scepticism and positivism. Universalism is very different from Berkeley's subjective Idealism (of which Dr Johnson said "I refute him thus", kicking a stone) which led to an objective or transcendental Idealism with Kant, who thought that the "transcendental ego" constructs knowledge out of sense impressions; and which led to the 19th century objective Idealism of Fichte and Schelling and the absolute Idealism of Hegel, which was followed by the British Hegelian Bradley. The tradition has been continued in Bergson's evolutionary intuitionism and in the process metaphysics or metaphysical Idealism of Whitehead, who was influenced by Bradley and created an Idealistic philosophy of science.

Universalism differs from Idealism in that whereas Idealism sees matter as composed of Idea, mind, consciousness or spirit, Universalism focuses on the Fire or Light as a universal energy which gives rise to both consciousness and matter. In so far as this mystic and metaphysical Reality of the Fire or Light is the spirit and consciousness it has given rise to, then it is closely linked to metaphysical Idealism, as is much Eastern mystical thinking: for example the Hindu Sankara, the Buddhist Asvaghosa and Asanga, and in recent times Aurobindo and Tagore; the Chinese Ch'an and Hui-neng (or Southern) schools and some Neo-Confucianist schools and Japanese Zen; and the Persian Jalal ad-Din ar-Rumi.

The Universalist view of man does not emphasise the reason, as does the rational approach to metaphysics of the Germans Leibniz and Kant. Metaphysics is the knowledge of the supersensible, and it is about a reality that is beyond the body and sense (Plato's unseen world of Forms which are beyond the world of appearances). Leibniz and Kant were Rationalists who adopted wrong approaches to metaphysics. Leibniz gave importance to mathematics and synthetic method; he researched into a universal cause of all Being, which reduced reasoning to mathematics, and saw reality as composed not of particles of matter but of centres of force or monads. (The word "monad" first appeared in 1695.) These monads are not physical in the sense that atoms are physical; they are metaphysical entities, local embodiments of force, each varying in power, each self-activating and self-sufficient and reflecting God, the Monad of monads. Each monad has perception, and the whole concept anticipates the "hidden variables" sought by Einstein and Bohm.

Kant correctly criticised all rational approaches to metaphysics as the "eye of reason" cannot, by its very nature, see into the spiritual realm, which is approached with the "eye of contemplation". Kant criticised Leibniz's method, arguing that rational knowledge of the supersensible is impossible as thinking has to be grounded in particulars and sense. He argued that metaphysics cuts itself off from sense experience in going behind it, not grasping that it is the eye of contemplation, not the eye of reason, which sees the supersensible. As a result of Kant, the rational approach to metaphysics became speculative and discredited while the contemplative approach to metaphysics fell into neglect.

It has been left to Universalism to existentialise the metaphysical Reality in the vision of the Fire or Light, which can be known as gnosis through experience rather than thought; and which can be seen with the eye of contemplation rather than the eye of reason. Universalism differs from the rational approach to metaphysics in that whereas the rational approach to metaphysics approached the universe through the rational, social ego, and sought the cause of being and related it to sense experience, Universalism goes behind the rational, social ego to the soul and surrenders to allow the Fire or Light to come in from above, manifesting downwards from the divine, through the spiritual, to the psychological and physical levels, and revealing the One cause of being (the Fire or Light) which is known beyond sense experience.

The Universalist view of man does not emphasise feeling and the imagination of Romantic man as does Romanticism, which is in fact a spiritual movement directed to the Light, to the invisible and to a sense of oneness with Nature. The Romantics, besides embodying a secular Evangelical religion of the heart, all wrote of their oneness with a vital Nature. Some of them were aware of the invisible through

Neoplatonism or German Idealism, some only of the visible. Wordsworth and Coleridge (who was in many ways Wordsworth's mentor and link to German metaphysics, the Transcendental Idealism of Kant and Fichte, before their tour of Germany in 1798-9), were both aware of the invisible or (to use Rilke's phrase) were "bees of the Invisible": Coleridge's "Ah! from the soul itself must issue forth/A light, a glory, a fair luminous cloud" and Wordsworth's "a dim and undetermined sense/Of unknown modes of being". (The unknown mode of Being was of a higher, vital invisible level than materialistic, mechanistic existence; a level in which a mountain could have a vital life of its own rather than be a heap of dead stones and rocks.) In the second generation of Romantics Shelley (who was influenced by Thomas Taylor the Platonist) carried on this sense of an invisible "white Radiance of Eternity", seeing an "unseen Power" which floats though unseen among us, (*Hymn to Intellectual Beauty*, 1816), and the universe which "flows through the mind" (*Mont Blanc*). Keats, however, was more attached to the world of phenomena and of the senses, and he was obsessed by the transience of life and of his own existence which was so poignantly summed up by his own epitaph: "Here lies one whose name was writ in water." Keats's ideal of Beauty may have had Platonic overtones (which he got from Bailey), but it was pretty much a phenomenal beauty. Byron was more a late Augustan in his concentration on the rational, social ego of Don Juan and his other heroes; rather than a Romantic of the invisible tradition.

The Light can be found in the Romantic tradition. Wordsworth is very aware of "a sense sublime/Of something.../Whose dwelling is the light of setting suns..../ A motion and a spirit that impels/All thinking things, all objects of all thought,/And rolls through all things" (*Tintern Abbey*, 1798). Coleridge defined the imagination in terms of the Light in *Dejection: an Ode* (1802), where "my shaping spirit of Imagination" (the unifying faculty according to *Biographia Literaria*, ch. 13) is equated with joy, which is also a "luminous mist", the Light. The Swedenborgian Blake of course was supremely aware of the fourfold vision of the Kabbalah and of the "intellectual vision" of the Light (letter to Hayley of 23rd October 1804). But in their work Coleridge, Wordsworth and Blake do not make a feature of the Fire or Light as being a universal energy in all cultures, nor do they focus more than fleetingly on the experience when "we are laid asleep/In body, and become a living soul" (*Tintern Abbey*). Much of the Romantic movement is devoted to feeling for solitaries and Nature, medieval settings and a desire to attain the impossible like Shelley's Alastor; not to the experience all religions have in common, the mystic Oneness.

The Romantic hero is aware of the unattainable vision and knows in agony that he can never attain it, whereas the Universalist vision is about attaining it now. Universalism differs from Romanticism in that whereas the Romantic vision comes fleetingly and spontaneously, catching its recipient unaware, who then pines because of the withdrawal of the vision in "grief" (Coleridge's *Dejection: An Ode*, 1802, and Wordsworth's *Ode, Intimations of Immortality*, 1805-6), the Universalist has a structure for attaining the vision through regular meditations. The Romantics pursued but never found their unattainable vision - Coleridge retired into opium and Christianity and held Wordsworth responsible for Sara Hutchinson's withdrawal, Wordsworth grew old as a distributor of stamps in the post office, and Keats and Shelley died young - and the Romantic movement ended in the defeatism of Wordsworth's: "We poets in our youth begin in gladness;/ But thereof comes in the end despondency and madness." The Universalist is not defeated but victorious in opening to the vision through the discipline of meditation.

The Universalist view of man does not emphasise the despair of Modernist man. Kermode's *Romantic Image* (1957) sees the Romantic movement as continuing in the Modernist movement of c1870-1930 (a view first stated in 1931 by Edmund Wilson in *Axel's Castle*). Kermode sees the Modernists as sharing the Romantic attitudes: the Romantic view of the artist as isolated and the Romantic focus on the image (as opposed to statement) and organic form. The Modernists celebrated the "epiphany" (the "revelation" of the symbol which Stephen explains to Cranly in Dublin's Eccles Street in Joyce's *Stephen Hero*). The Feast of the Epiphany on January 6th celebrates the arrival of the three kings at the manger, where they saw a baby, but also something more. The Modernist epiphany is of the invisible, of an invisible beauty: Joyce's wading girl ("Heavenly God! cried Stephen's soul, in an outburst of profane joy", *Portrait of the Artist as a Young Man*), Eliot's rose garden, Pound's image like a Chinese hieroglyph, which looks what it means. Like the Romantics, the Modernists smashed principally because they did not solve the Romantic problem of the invisible. Eliot's attempted solution ended in conventional Christianity (the unconventional central vision of which is the central idea of our civilisation), Pound retreated into sympathy with Italian (agrarian) Fascism, and Yeats was diverted into occult theories about the phases of the moon. The Modernists protested at the horror of modern industrial civilisation and the aimlessness and futility of modern life (Eliot's *Waste Land*, Kafka, Beckett). With the exception of Eliot, their search ended in failure.

Like the Romantics, the Modernists have left the Universalist movement to solve the problems they never finally solved: approaching the invisible reality on a regular basis, with control, moving back from the rational, social ego to the soul. Universalism differs from Modernism in that whereas Modernism emphasised despair and saw the epiphany as an escape from a nihilistic, chaotic background, Universalism locates the soul many Modernists forgot they had, and contemplates the invisible reality through regular meditations which open the "eye of contemplation".

The Universalist view of man does not emphasise the outer freedom of Existentialist man. The Existentialists' insistence on the experiential is valuable, but being centred in the rational, social ego they recorded negative emotions of fear, dread, trembling, angst and vastation rather than positive joy. Existentialism gàthered strength in occupied France during the Second World War. Its philosophy of extremes was resonant when Europe was threatened with material and spiritual destruction and optimism seemed inappropriate, but like Romanticism it ended in despair.

Existentialism went wrong because it was based on the choosing rational, social ego in the visible world rather than on the soul or transcendental ego or universal being or essence which can know the invisible metaphysical Reality. The first Existentialists Kierkegaard and Nietzsche were not aware of moving back to the soul although they questioned reason (as did Dostoevsky's *Underground Man*). To the phenomenologist Husserl ontology is objects of consciousness in the "lived world" (Lebenswelt), and there is a transcendental or absolute ego which is a true source of of all meaning. Heidegger, Husserl's pupil, jettisoned consciousness and the transcendental ego and proposed an ontology of human being ("Dasein") in which man (i.e. man's rational, social ego) is a subject and cannot be made an object. He held that no man can purify his own thinking to become an absolute ego, refusing to realise that there is a divine part of man which is absolute; and that this is located in the silence behind language and that man can purify his own mind and become a transcendental or absolute ego. Heidegger held that the world can be understood only as it appears, that the real is within appearances. In fact the real comes into consciousness as the mystic Fire or Light. Jaspers in *On my Philosophy* (also translated as *Existenzphilosophie*), 1941, writes of "man and Transcendence (or: the soul and the Deity)" and states: "Transcendence (Deity) ...alone is the real Being." Marcel, the author of *A Metaphysical Journal*, was on the right lines, but his evidence is untrustworthy because of his Christian doctrine.

Sartre, like Heidegger, denied the existence of the "transcendental ego" or universal being or soul. All

WHAT IS UNIVERSALISM?

Sartre's heroes are soulless: M. Roquentin feels nausea at his own existence - Sartre had taken LSD before his own experience of nausea. Camus's heroes are just as soulless: in *L'Etranger* Camus's Meursault drifts at the level of the rational, social ego in a dead "indifferent" universe, not a loving one. Sartre wrote "Existence before essence"; in other words, a thing exists before it has an essence, by which Sartre meant a plan in the mind of its maker, and if man exists before he has an essence or nature then he has no maker. In fact, had Sartre got behind the contingent rational, social ego, which sees meaninglessness, to the universal being, and had he opened to the mystical, metaphysical Light which is present throughout the universe, he would have understood that "essence before existence" is a more accurate slogan, that the essence or universal being which knows the Light takes precedence over the existing personality or rational, social ego.

Existentialism went further wrong because it was based on the lowest of the four levels of manifested metaphysical reality: Existence (rather than Being). Sartre and Camus recognise Existence, of course, but not Being in its metaphysical sense. They see Being as a Nothingness, i.e. possible existence or man's possibilities which are absurd, but they think of Being in terms of the lowest level of reality. Sartre wrote *Being and Nothingness* but he confuses "Being" and "Existence". In its metaphysical sense (as used by Guénon for example in *The Multiple States of Being*) Being is a level above Existence and contains all the potentialities of Existence; it is the oneness behind all different, particular existents. Heidegger and Sartre, in short, confused their Being with their Becoming or their Existence.

Universalism differs from Existentialism in that whereas Existentialism's subject is Existence as perceived by the rational, social ego, Universalism focuses on Being as perceived by the soul - on Being as the Light. Whereas Existentialism dispenses with the self as a fixed entity, and with consciousness and epistemology or knowing, because man is a free agent without a fixed nature like a tree or stone who makes himself by his choices, Universalism focuses on the inner self as a new centre which can know the Light of Reality by an epistemology of illumination.

Existentialism, which is principally about the rational, social ego and Existence rather than about the soul or universal being and Being, has reached an end and is dying. It is being replaced by a post-Existentialism, Universalism, which *is* about the universal being and its universal existential confrontation with the Fire or Light. This post-Existentialist, Universalist view of man, solves the problems of Existentialism, escaping despair and negative emotions by moving behind the nihilistic rational, social ego and contacting Supreme Being. At the same time Universalism existentialises the rational approach to metaphysics and offers a regularly attainable invisible Reality in place of the fleetingly glimpsed and unattainable epiphanies and apparently insoluble problems that destroyed the Romantics and the Modernists. Universalism is the heir to the tradition of Leibniz and Whitehead, Wordsworth, Coleridge and Shelley, Eliot and Yeats, Husserl and Marcel.

The new vision of man that Universalism proclaims shows all men as open to forces in the universe; filled with the guiding energy of the Light, their souls open to these forces. It offers a view of man who has a constant dialogue with the Light. To consider this we need to consider the new view of the universe which makes such a dialogue possible.

*

The new cosmological view of the universe of Universalism differs from the scientific materialistic view of the universe of the last 300 years. The universe of rationalism, materialism, humanism and scepticism is a dead one, a mechanistic one, and some modern scientists have seen this view as positivist, objectivist and reductionist. The new view of the universe is in the vitalist tradition of Bergson, Hulme and Whitehead (and Sheldrake). It sees the universe as being filled with an energy which pervades all existing things. But Universalism is not just vitalism. It differs from vitalism in that vitalism posits a Life-Force or "élan vital" whereas Universalism sees this energy as the Fire of Heracleitus, the Fire or Light (a perception which also distinguishes Universalist cosmology from other cosmologies).

This energy, once known as ether and in India as prana, is in fact the Fire or Light which is everywhere. It comes from the One, the transcendent made immanent, and pervades the quantum vacuum which is present both where I am writing and where you are reading. It is present in creation as Being, the potentialities of existence, and it is present in Existence. It is behind Nature and is the reality of the microworld. It is a concept of the universe as a sea of energy, the tides of which flow into us. As I put it in *A Metaphysical in Marvell's Garden*:

"With drowsed eyes glance at solid grass and be
In whirlpools of energy like a sea.
Breaths heave the light, and answering currents
                    pour
Through spongy stones and stars, or seaweed tree.
Now see with eye of mind into swelled form,
Imagine sap wash, oak wave in acorn.
Knowers are one with known, and are soaked by
                    tides
That foam and billow through an ebbing lawn."

The Universalist vision of the universe is an optimistic one, for it has an optimistic belief in an infinite principle. It sees this energy as being filled with wisdom, understanding, love and thought, and to some extent it draws on the Idealism of New Thought (that the universe is a network of Universal Mind or Intelligence). In New Thought psychological thought governs physical acts. (Say "I am healthy" or "I am prosperous" and New Thought maintains the affirmed condition happens.) At a higher level a spiritual influx from the infinite governs the psychological thoughts. At a higher level still the One Light governs spiritual influxes. There are different levels, but Truth is indivisible. It cannot be cut up so that lower psychological thought and action are separated from higher divine and spiritual Light. Such a cutting up is the humanist fallacy. People know that a statement of a divided truth of the Light is partial, emasculated, dud. They need the whole truth. A quotation from the *New Testament* is relevant: "Except a corn of wheat fall into the ground and die, it abideth alone: but if it die, it bringeth forth much fruit." All who are ready to die into the ground of the tradition, Universalism, find they bring forth much fruit. Whereas those who abide alone at the humanist's psychological and physical levels remain separated from their spiritual and divine roots in the tradition, and "abide alone" like a seed on waste land that has not taken root and grown into corn-bearing wheat.

The Universalist vision of such a living universe has to take account of the relativity and quantum accounts of the origin of the universe. The traditional 20th century picture of the origin of the universe is through relativity. Before the Big Bang, Einstein's equations tell us, space was tightly wrapped round itself into a self-contained ball of matter, energy, space and time - the cosmic egg, the primeval atom, singularity, a point of infinite density and zero volume. Because is was compressed space was hotter than it is now. When this exploded, space itself expanded and was stretched. One tenth of a second after the beginning the temperature was 30 billion degrees Kelvin and the universe consisted of a mixture of very high energy radiation (photons) and material particles including neutrons, protons and electrons. One second later the temperature had cooled to 10 billion degress Kelvin; the reactions between particles was similar to the nuclear reactions that go on around the sun today. After 14 seconds it was 3 billion degrees Kelvin.

Add the quantum rules to relativity's account of the beginning as Hawking did, and then the edges (the beginning and end of time) can disappear, leaving no boundaries. So how did it get so large? Inflation. The vacuum of the universe was unstable and according to one view (and this is the beginning of the materialistic nightmare) enough energy was created to squeeze some matter into forming a black hole. This led to the creation of a black hole. If all the matter in the universe were collected at a single point its negative energy would cancel out the positive mass energy of all matter.

What is clear is that the universe started in a point of zero energy which became separated into matter with positive energy and gravity with negative energy - the gravity coming from the geometric curvature of space.

What is our universe? After the discoveries of Hawking (who has been called the Einstein of our time) and others, one recent theory which leads to the materialistic nightmare is that it is a large black hole, with space-time forming a self-contained closed entity folded round it and held together by gravity and superstrings of quarks with 26 dimensions, only 4 of which are known, which unify quantum theory, general relativity, black holes, the beginning of time and gravity. It has no boundaries of space, which is curved, and operates self-balancingly through zero gravity. There can be an infinite number of universes (Everett's further nightmarish idea) which also come out of reality, a superdense concentrate of mass smaller than a proton but containing no energy because the positive energy of mass is balanced by negative gravitational energy, and growing through inflation; and as there is no beginning in time there is no creator, this view of Hawking's alleges.

To David Bohm we are in a multidimensional reality from which there is an unfolding of an implicate order, and matter and consciousness both unfold from this sea of energy and must be understood in relation to the implicate order and the whole. The cosmos is a vast sea of energy to Bohm, who is deconstructing modern science. Bohm, who has been influenced by Krishnamurti, is similar to Derrida in examining the presuppositions of Western philosophy and culture from within; but whereas Derrida reduces everything to texts as a reductionist linguistic analyst and is attacking a hidden metaphysical agenda in certain key concepts of Western philosophy, Bohm questions the mechanistic and reductionist basis of the formulas and structures of our "fragmented thinking" (Bohm's term) which do not correspond to the nature of reality - which is whole. For Bohm, quantum physics suggests a new way of thinking about order that extends beyond the limits of subatomic physics, and that even randomness is a kind of order.

If we put these two views together, we get a multidimensional whole reality from whose sea of energy matter and consciousness unfold and to which they return. This could have, but need not have, originated in a point; negative and positive energy balancing each other, and being separated into matter (with positive energy) and gravity (with negative energy); all you need is enough energy to squeeze matter into forming a black hole. According to Hawking the point must have come from a previous universe. Bohm says we can never understand reality in terms of particles and fields alone, but we must ultimately perceive wholeness in a non-reductionist way.

The Universalist vision of the universe takes account of these theories, but also of the most up to date research in quantum physics. It combines relativity and some aspects of quantum theory. What do contemporary quantum physicists like the Brussels-based Edgard Gunzig, convener of conferences for the world's leading physicists who works closely with the E.C. authorities, have to say about how the universe emerged from the quantum vacuum? Real nothing becomes a quantum vacuum by quantum processes through virtual particles. Real nothing is emptiness. By principle a vacuum is non-empty. It has an underground life but is the most possible emptiness that can be imagined; i.e. it is as close to an absence of particles and radiation as can be imagined, it is the lowest possible energy state. Virtual particles do not exist as such, they are *potentialities of being* (which are found in the void). What is a particle? Is it defined mathematically in a universal way or is it to be detected by a detector? As a vacuum is the lowest possible energy state, observers in relativity with constant velocity see the same vacuum. But an accelerating observer sees himself surrounded by a cloud of particles. Again, what is a particle? Is it the response of an excited detector or is it something else?

A vacuum trembles through the gravitation of the curvature of space, which is a reservoir of energy that can be given to virtual particles. These virtual particles are expelled from the vacuum in pairs and return - but add energy from the curvature of space and you have a real particle which could be a first proton which could turn into photons. When virtual particles join existence they become real particles or photons; after which they cannot be undone. Virtual particles can become real particles by taking energy from the geometric curvature of space, according to tests with electric fields in laboratories. But was space curved in the vacuum before the beginning of time? Was it wrapped round itself like a cosmic egg? Physicists will say this is an "epistemological and philosophical" question, that it is at present the centre of a great debate between several schools, including the Cambridge school of Hawking, the Oxford school of Penrose and schools in the United States. Physicists say that the problem is not solved but they are sure gravitation is not working in the vacuum. There are different formulae and "you can't prove or disprove any statements concerning these things". Such statements indeed express a point of view relating to aesthetical and internal coherence; they do not prove anything, we do not really know, there is no conclusion. Physicists such as Bryce DeWitt have been working in this field for 40 years and have not been able to come up with the answers.

What does contemporary cosmology say about the beginning? There is no need for a Big Bang. As we have just seen a quantum vacuum can pre-exist a Big Bang. Cosmic background radiation, the hiss discovered by Penzias and Wilson in 1964/5, is not the residue of the Big

Bang. It *is* left over from near the beginning. When in density and heat the universe expanded, the temperature went down and several atomic processes were possible, the main one being the capture of free electrons by hydrogen and helium nuclei, as a result of which photons decoupled from the electrons and propagated freely in straight lines until they reached our telescopes. These photons originated in the cooling and recombination period c300,000 to 500,000 years *after* the beginning. There is no need for a Big Bang. All you need is a hot beginning (Fire?) - very dense, very hot conditions - and inflation does the rest, expanding seeds in the microworld to galaxies in our universe. At the beginning (if that is the word) there was real nothing - not a vacuum, nothing, and no time; due to quantum processes, a quantum vacuum emerged, and space and space-time, as virtual particles became real. "Beginning" is tautologous, the idea of a beginning is suspect; time begins when the quantum begins, there is no singularity (or point in space-time at which the space-time curvature becomes infinite), no first proton.

And boundaries - what do contemporary physicists say about boundaries of space and time? There is a semantic problem in talking of boundaries, in saying that the universe has no boundaries. If space is seen as a two-dimensional sphere then it has a finite surface without borders, and all paths are of finite length; it is like walking round the earth and you always come back to where you started. Space is finite but without boundary. Expand it, and it is still finite. If space is seen as a two-dimensional plane, however, then every path leads to infinity, and boundaries are not important. Shrink the plane and it is still infinite. So space can be finite like a sphere or infinite like a plane. In fact, it is most likely to be hyperboloid. And what of the boundary of time? Is there eternity? Timelessness? We can pose the question in a rational framework, but the answers depend on what we are calling an end or a beginning.

The picture of how the universe developed is now regarded to have been as follows. First there was real nothing: darkness everywhere. This nothing was a vacuum which is by definition unstable. The instability led to pairs of virtual particles - particles which have a potentiality - being expelled. Normally these live for a split second and then return to the quantum vacuum. If one of the pair attracts energy from the geometric background of the curvature of space, then it becomes a real particle. With this process happening simultaneously in different parts of the quantum vacuum, then, there were numerous real particles with positive energy, created by negative energy from the curvature of space, so that the universe has expanded from zero energy. Out of this grew a hot beginning. From this point to the beginning of inflation has been understood; the mathematics for this has been done by the Brussels school associated with Edgard Gunzig. They were awarded the Gravity Research Foundation International Award (on one of three occasions Gunzig has received this prestigious award) for the mathematics but only in 1992 did they realise that their solution could be applied to explaining inflation. In all likelihood inflation caused seeds in the microworld to expand and become the seeds of galaxies, and these are associated with the ripple effect in the discovery of Smoot and Mather. This discovery (at a temperature of 10^{-6}) suggests that there is dark matter in the universe. It shows that in all probability the universe will expand for ever and will not contract to a Big Crunch. Everything points to an open, not a closed universe, i.e. one in the shape of a hyperboloid or hyperplane, not a sphere. And the search is now on for dark matter.

Such a view of real nothing, a quantum vacuum and the emergence of a phenomenal world reminds me of an Eastern equation, written out for me by Japan's most famous poet and included as a pentameter in my poem *The Silence* (1965-6): $+A + -A = 0$, great zero. To put it the other way round, real nothing = quantum vacuum (-A) + the phenomenal world (+A), or Non-Being and Being. Such a view also recalls Bohm. Many physicists now look on Bohm with respect, as the current view of the origin of the universe is approaching Bohm's: a concrete unfolding from an implicate order within the quantum vacuum.

I must point out that this (so far as we know) correct view of the universe as coming from the quantum vacuum conflicts with the classical theory of general relativity, which, as Hawking and Penrose showed, requires a beginning of time in a point of infinite density and infinite curvature of space-time, where all the known laws of science break down. According to relativity, as we have seen, our universe began as a superdense concentration of mass smaller than a proton (Dante's "infinitesimal point") and containing zero energy because the positive energy of mass is balanced by negative gravitational energy, and expanded through inflation. This correct view also to some extent conflicts with Hawking's materialistic and reductionist forecast of the quantum theory of gravity (a complete and consistent theory of which is still being sought) in which the universe did not begin with a single proton, and had no beginning in time or singularity at which the laws of science broke down; and therefore had no creator, no God. We have seen that to Hawking the universe is a large black hole in reverse, expanding rather than contracting, with space-time forming a closed entity folded round it. It is held together by gravity and superstrings, and has no boundaries of space, which is curved. (We have already considered boundaries. It is interesting that John Barrow says in *Theories of Everything* that Hawking's "no boundary condition" is picked out only for aesthetic reasons, and is not demanded by the internal logical consistency of the quantum universe.) Hawking's interpretation of the discovery of Smoot and Mather suggests that a Big Crunch is coming[3], but as we have just seen, it isn't.

So where does the Fire fit into all this? A Universalist Fire-based account of the origin and structure of the universe is as follows. The universe began when the transcendent Fire in real nothing made the quantum vacuum unstable and threw out virtual particles, potentialities of Being. The Fire is present in the vacuum and in the air in differing intensities and may account for the uneven performance of electrons. The Fire is common in all particles that came from the quantum vacuum and which came from outer space (e.g. gamma photons). It is therefore immanent in the seeds of galaxies and stars, Nature and consciousness. It is therefore present in Existence.

The Fire or Light offers a new view of the universe because it is the universal experience of mystics that the Fire or Light that pervades the universe is filled with wisdom and understanding and love which can flow into man. It seems that the universe is a living universe of Higher Thought, Universal Mind, Universal Intelligence and Universal Wisdom.

The new view of man in the universe, then, is of man like a sponge, filled in his soul with tides of Light that permeate the quantum vacuum and pervade creation and Nature in a metaphysical scheme of manifestation. Just as the universe emerged from the quantum vacuum, so did we. We live in a quantum vacuum - we are surrounded by virtual particles, they are in the air - and we are in a quantum vacuum now, in a sea of cosmic energy, only *we* are real particles.

The Universalist view of the universe takes its inspiration from the universe that existed before scientific materialism, and it draws on the vitalist, organicist tradition that has survived during the last 300 years. In the last 300 years separatism, mechanism and reductionism have removed man from the centre of the universe to a marginal irrelevance on the edge. First Copernicus decentralised the earth in favour of the sun; then Descartes decentralised the soul in favour of the reason (the rational, social ego); then Darwin decentralised man in favour of the ape from which he originated, so that man became an offshoot of the ape; then Freud decentralised the conscious mind in favour of the unconscious; and now the space probes of our own time have put this emasculated, material, man-ape on just one of trillions of stars.

The living tides known to the mystical vision, the metaphysical structure of the universe and the restoration of the soul, however, all put man back at the centre of the universe, a position which is supported by the Anthropic Principle. After 20 years of flying between moons and planets it seems that the earth is the only star which provides an atmosphere and life for man, who has an immortal soul which he can contact behind his reason and his conscious mind. Descartes, Darwin and Freud were not telling the whole truth, and Copernicus's discovery has not shaken the uniqueness of man in the universe. Man counts again, his life has meaning and purpose again, and 300 years of scientific materialism have failed to diminish him. Within the one scheme, man and Nature and science are at one, and are not in conflict. All are a part of one. Consciousness is an important part of the whole and cannot be left out of the total view as an intruding or intrusive feature.

It is interesting that the man whose undergraduate work began the 300 year long era of scientific materialism, Isaac Newton, spent the rest of his life trying to establish such a total view of consciousness in the universe in terms of Light. Newton's attempt goes back to the beginnings of the Royal Society which were full of the esoteric tradition of Freemasonry, Rosicrucianism, Neoplatonism and Hermeticism. Newton, having established the mechanistic world view with his discoveries in gravity, light and calculus in 1664-6, in 1669 (at the age of 26) bought books on alchemy and unsuccessfully spent the next 30 years of his life seeking for an expanding force which would counteract gravity and offer a Grand Unified Theory of science. The Newton of "Newton's sleep" (Blake's words) in fact saw science as metaphysical.

In this later metaphysical, alchemistic period, Newton associated the "expanding force" for which he unsuccessfully searched with light. David Castillejo writes in *The Expanding Force of Newton's Cosmos*: "The contracting force in Newton's world is gravitation, which tends to draw all bodies together. But he also seems to have sought a single expanding force in the cosmos. This force, the law it obeys, and the structures it builds, can best be observed by following the progress of a ray of light." From his study of polarised light, Newton deduced that "every Ray may be considered as having four Sides or Quarters", i.e. each ray of light is four-sided (cf the four Kabbalistic worlds). He held that this single expanding force operates in the radiation of light, in chemical composition and in biological growth, and also governs the mind and behaviour of human beings. In query 30 of *Opticks* Newton asked: "Are not gross Bodies and Light convertible into one Another and may not Bodies receive much of their Activity from the particles of Light which enter their Composition?" In an alchemical manuscript now in the Burndy Library, he states that "Ether is but a vehicle of some more active spirit & the bodies may be concreted of both together" (i.e. ether and spirit), "they may imbibe ether well (sic) as air in generation & in the ether the spirit is entangled. This spirit is the body of light because both have a prodigious active principle."

In other words, the later Newton is saying that the Light combines with ether (which Einstein in 1905 showed was unnecessary when he showed that light behaves as if all its energy is concentrated in quantum packets of energy now called photons) - Bohm's sea of cosmic energy - and creates spirit, souls and bodies, and he was thus proposing a single unified system in which the internal and external systems were linked. I have a poem about Newton's expanding force, called *Cambridge Ode: Against Materialism (or Newton's Enlightenment)*. Newton's view that light is a beam of complex and heterogeneous rays has been the foundation of physical optics since his time, although he was atomistic (and reductionist) in insisting that individual rays of light have immutable properties, i.e. immutable particles of matter.

In a sense Newton's idea was taken up by Einstein, who proposed that as gravity attracts, there is a force that repels and balances everything. Einstein called it the cosmological constant (1917). Einstein's cosmological constant was a repulsive force of unknown origin which exactly balances the attraction of gravitation of all matter and keeps the universe static. To put it other terms, the cosmological constant was an expanding force of the Fire or Light that counteracted the contracting force of gravity, and which gave all particles stable interconnectedness for all time. Einstein abandoned the cosmological constant - he called his abandonment the "biggest blunder of my life" - when Hubble observed that the universe was expanding, but it now seems that this constant had a role at the beginning of the universe: recent theoretical physics suggest that in the early universe the cosmological constant may have had a nonzero value which may have been connected with the precise nature of the vacuum state.

Einstein's work on the cosmological constant must be seen alongside his unfinished search for "hidden variables", the hidden principle which causes one nucleus to decay and not another, and underlies the indeterminacy of the uncertainty principle (see pages 15-16). Einstein never found any hidden variables, and Niels Bohr and his Copenhagen school rejected hidden variables as quantities that could not be measured. In 1935 Einstein came up with the Einstein-Podolsky-Rosen thought experiment, which Bohm later improved. Bohm wrote a book on quantum theory in 1951, and in January 1952 first took Einstein's side and rebelled against the other physicists in an article in *Physical Review* (two papers published together) entitled *A Suggested Interpretation of the Quantum Theory in Terms of "Hidden" Variables.*

In his article Bohm says that the usual interpretation of the quantum theory is self-consistent but it involves an assumption that it cannot be tested experimentally, that the physical state of an individual system is completely specified by a wave function that determines only probable results of actual measurement processes. Bohm argues that the only way of investigating the truth of this assumption is by trying to find some other interpretation of the quantum theory in terms of at present "hidden" variables, which in principle determine the precise behaviour of an individual system. Bohm suggests an interpretation of the quantum theory in terms of such "hidden" variables, and shows that as long as the mathematical theory retains its present form, this suggested interpretation leads to the same results for all physical processes as does the usual interpretation - while offering a broader conceptual framework and eliminating some of the difficulties of the existing theory involving distances of 10^{-13}cm or less.

Bohm points out that Einstein always believed that even at the quantum level there must exist precisely definable elements or dynamical variables that determine the actual behaviour of each individual system, and not merely its probable behaviour; and that while Einstein admitted the internal consistency of the quantum theory, he regarded its present form as incomplete. Bohm's alternative interpretation allows each individual system to be conceived as being in a precisely definable state whose changes are determined by definite laws. After the completion of his article Bohm's attention was drawn to de Broglie's similar alternative interpretation of the quantum theory in 1926. De Broglie later abandoned this following criticisms by Pauli and following objections from himself. Bohm shows that all these criticisms and objections could have been met if de Broglie had carried his ideas to their logical conclusion.

As Bohm points out, the consistency of the quantum theory does not exclude the possibility of other equally consistent interpretations, which would not require us to forgo seeing the quantum level in precise terms. To opt for the present quantum theory limits our choice of alternative theories or interpretations which may give better understandings. One such interpretation allows simultaneous measurements of position and motion to have unlimited precision and may lead to new effects in respect of distances less than 10^{-13}cm that are not consistent with the present quantum theory. In his second paper Bohm shows that von Neumann's "proof" that quantum theory is not consistent with hidden variables does not apply to his interpretation because the hidden variables at short distances go beyond von Neumann's assumptions. Bohm points out that the usual interpretation of quantum theory "seems to have been guided to a considerable extent by the principle of not postulating the possible existence of entities that cannot now be observed", a principle that stems from positivitism or empiricism. ("Entities that cannot now be observed" recall Leibniz's monads. In *Wholeness and the Implicate Order* Bohm compares his notion of "moments" to Leibniz's monads, each of which mirrors the whole in its own way, but makes clear that his moments or entities do not have permanent existence, as do monads.)

The way forward would be to "postulate that the precise outcome of each individual measurement process is in principle determined by some at present 'hidden' elements or variables; and we could then try to find experiments that depended in a unique and reproducible way on the assumed state of these hidden elements or variables. If such predictions are verified, we should then obtain experimental evidence favouring the hypothesis that hidden variables exist."

To strengthen Bohm's objections to the present quantum theory it should be pointed out that quantum mechanics is not a physical theory at all, but a mathematical theory - a point that has been corroborated by Brian Josephson (at a symposium in January 1986): "quantum mechanics is a mathematical theory"; by N.F. Mott (in his book *Elements of Wave Mechanics*, 1962): "wave mechanics is a system of equations"; and by Anthony Deakin (talk in September 1991): "Quantum theory is merely a set of recipes.... One can't reason into it too closely - as then there would be nothing left."[4]

Bohm stuck on his position for the next forty years, introducing the implicate order in *Wholeness and the Implicate Order*, 1980, chapter 4 of which, "Hidden variables in the quantum theory", presents the mathematics for a "sub-quantum-mechanical level involving hidden variables" and discusses experiments to probe the sub-quantum level. Meanwhile the Aspect experiment of 1981-82 to verify Bell's theorem was widely interpreted as making a reality in the microworld impossible. In fact, as Willis Harman states of the Aspect experiment in his *A Re-examination of the Metaphysical Foundations of Modern Science*: "The result showed quite conclusively that if we want to speak of an objective 'reality' behind the appearances, then that reality must be interconnected over all space and time. Any two particles that have once interacted must continue to be connected in some way for the rest of time. This means that all particles in the universe are interconnected. These interconnections are very difficult to conceive of in terms of the ordinary world of things and their interactions. They act instantaneously, are not mediated by fields of any kind, and do not diminish with distance." Such a view confirms rather than denies Bohm's view of an implicate reality or order within a wholeness, and also makes possible a reality that is filled with the Fire or Light as the mystic One or the metaphysical Reality.

Such a reality in the microworld raises the question of the origin of mass in relation to Dark Matter and of the most modern particle-collider. At present we can only account for one tenth of all matter. Nine-tenths seems to be invisible "Dark Matter". Recent tests coming from the Large Electron-Positron Collider (LEP) at CERN, the European laboratory for Particle Physics in Geneva, suggest that there is a new family of subatomic particles, "supersymmetrical" particles, of which Dark Matter may be made. We now know what the building blocks of matter are (fermions), but we do not know why they have widely differing masses. (Some are thousands of times heavier than others of the same size.) The universe has the form it does because particles have the masses they do. Everything fits together, and any variation in the masses would affect the form the universe has. It is possible that there is a particle which gives all other particles their masses. This theory was first put forward by Peter

Higgs of Edinburgh University, and so this particle is called the "Higgs" particle.

I would propose that the Fire or Light is the invisible force which manifests into Dark Matter and gives all particles their masses, just as within the quantum vacuum it contains knowledge about all possible particles which can exist and has the seeds or germs for their potential creation. The Big Bang could have been the result of a "decision" by the Fire or Light within the quantum vacuum to release this potential. The origin of mass, Dark Matter and the true nature of the vacuum can therefore all be understood in relation to the Fire or Light. The building of Europe's Large Hadron Collider (LHC) in Geneva, the best ever particle smasher, can operate at higher energies than have ever been achieved, and can recreate the conditions and particles in the universe a millionth of a millionth of a second after the Big Bang, and can follow the evolution of these particles and identify supersymmetrical particles - and perhaps the consequences on electrons of the physically invisible Fire or Light.

Both Newton and Einstein, the two greatest geniuses in physics, left unfinished business, as has Bohm in our own time. It has been left to us - and to Universalism - to take up Newton's expanding force (possibly a fifth force), Einstein's balancing reality within the microworld, Bohm's view of a hidden variable and Higgs's view of the origin of mass, and give them new urgency in a new vision of the universe.

The Universalist universe, then, is a quantum universe filled with the metaphysical principle of an expanding Fire or Light, a force which may be responsible for the inflation that has led to our permanently expanding universe.

*

We have considered Universalism in relation to a changed view of man and a changed view of the universe, and our findings are at variance with the consensus view of modern science and philosophy, which as a result, quite simply, will have to follow suit and change.

Most modern scientists proceed through what St Bonaventure called the eye of the flesh (i.e. the world of the senses) and the eye of reason (experiment, verification, observation, testing, mathematics, predictability, logical coherence and hypothesis). Generally, the eye of reason guides the flesh, concept guides percept. If the eye of the flesh and the eye of reason are the way of the traffic jam and the motorway, there is another way, that of the helicopter: the eye of contemplation, with its intuition and a long tradition. This is a direct route, and reaches Truth. Most scientists start from separateness, mechanism and reductionism, i.e. the view that consciousness is separate from reality in a way that recalls Cartesian dualism; that the universe is to be understood as if it is a machine with cogs, not as a vital living thing; and that the scientist is only interested in parts, or bits of matter which lead to large lumps of matter and consciousness in a universe whose fundamental nature is granular.

Reductionism understands the whole by examining the parts. In the 19th century version of T.H. Huxley, it reduces all biological and mental events to physical events, which are in return reduced to properties of matter-energy. The divine and spiritual are reduced to the psychological, which is in turn reduced to the physical and subatomic. As a result humanity is reduced within a Nature and universe which are deterministic, immutable and non-anthropocentric. Reductionist thinking gives: a universe made up of particles; physical bodies that are collections of atoms; and thoughts that are combinations of sense impressions alone, or words.

In philosophy, which supplies theories about the universe of science, reductionism can be found in logical positivism, which defined expressions of existing things, states of affairs and scientific facts in terms of observable objects, sense data or observation reports. Thus every statement is equivalent to, and can be reduced to, a set of empirically verifiable statements. Linguistic analysis similarly sees statements in terms of combinations of words, and reductionism became deconstruction with Derrida, who carried this process further by undermining philosophical statements in terms of key component words. This reductionist view is quite wrong as language, although learned from without, is inspired by organic patterns that grow from within, is vital, and covers the whole cultural tradition, including inner concepts which are not subject to empirical observation or listing.

Derrida's deconstruction is in fact at the heart of a cluster of linguistic movements which have undermined Western values to little purpose. Structuralism began in the 1960s with de Saussure and Lévi-Strauss. Deconstruction formed later in the 1960s when Derrida and de Man criticised Structuralism, especially Lévi-Strauss; drew on Heidegger's "Destruktion" (destruction) of ontology in favour of Dasein; and dissolved the borders between linguistics, literary criticism and philosophy. This mixture resulted in Post-Structuralism in the 1970s with Roland Barthes, moved away from the unified person and drew on psychoanalysis. Post-Modernism in literature evolved from it with the undermining of the unified narrator, image-management and focus on how the author tells a story.

There has got to be a change in science and philosophy, and in the philosophy of science, as the view of the consensus of scientists is out of date. The message to be got across is that the separatist, mechanistic and reductionist scientific view of the universe no longer works; that seeing reality as particles and subparticles alone is wrong. Rather science is vitalist or organicist, involving process and self-organising invisible "spirit". An anti-reductionist, more relational view of Nature has arisen as a result of new studies in matter, living systems and mind-brain relationships. In biology the living cell is more than its molecules, it is a self-organising process (as we are ourselves) which manifests from the whole downwards from universals to particulars. Nature consists of events and their relationships - process - rather than of separate substances and particles, and in both physics and biology reductionism is being undermined, by quantum physics and by the teleological principle in evolution. Particles seen as particles are non-processive, but through Young's "two slits" experiment, they can be shown to be a process of disturbing the environment rather than as individual particles or waves. In other words, particles should not be seen as particles or waves, but as events. Vitalism or organicism is the view of Bergson, Hulme in his vitalist Bergsonian period, and the later Whitehead of *Process and Reality* (1929). The message to be got across is that separatist, mechanistic and reductionist science and philosophy have been successful but their time is up; and that a new wholeness science and philosophy can supplement it and replace it. In other words that there has got to be a paradigm shift, a shift in scientists' reality, values and goals.

How can this message be got across to today's scientists? One approach is to go to where they are and take them one step further forward, to speak in neutral terms, concentrating on epistemology rather than on ontology or a definite view of reality, dealing in postulates or models including all interpretations of truth (with a small t) and ignoring Truth. A symposium on reductionism, such as the one held at Cambridge in September 1992 with an array of scientists and philosophers including Roger Penrose, Mary Midgley and John Barrow, is one way of doing this. Another way can be found in Willis Harman's *A Re-examination of the Metaphysical Foundations of Modern Science* (1991). Harman uses the reason to approach the ontological and epistemological foundations of science and concludes that moves to a wholeness science may stimulate research in the entire spectrum of states of consciousness, including "'religious experiences', experiences of 'mystical' states of consciousness and of 'other dimensions of reality'. These experiences have been at the heart of all cultures, including our own." (These sentences make me wonder if he was thinking of *The Fire and the Stones* when he wrote them.) His conclusion falls short of getting us to the starting point, the shift from the "eye of reason" to the "eye of contemplation", but it does move the scientist on a step, from separatism, mechanism and reductionism to an awareness to something beyond. This is the gradualistic (or moderate) approach. Its disadvantage is that it starts with separatism, mechanism and reductionism and takes them a little further forward instead of embarking on a clean sweep and overthrowing the wrong assumptions of science. In the history of thought an abrupt or sudden change is regarded as a revolution, and Thomas Kuhn in *The Structure of Scientific Revolutions* (second edition 1970) saw the history of science as proceeding through occasional revolutions which are punctuated by periods of consolidation or "normal science".

In science there needs to be a revolution which leads to the new way of looking, an announcement of abrupt change that would get across to the universities. Ideally, students should discard their tutors with contempt if they will not change (an act requiring considerable courage) and bright research students and younger academics need to be disturbed by the new vision. Realistically, such things will not happen as students have to conform to obtain their degrees and young academics are understandably reluctant to risk losing their jobs and damaging their careers. An abrupt change can only be set in motion by someone outside the system, who is not beholden to it or dependent on it for a living, whose career is not at stake and who can speak up for the truth. That is where I come in. At a gathering of nine philosophers investigating the metaphysical foundations of modern science in a garden in Hampshire in June 1992, with peacocks screaming round our feet and from a nearby rooftop, I urged those present to use the eye of their reason to "question Heisenberg's uncertainty principle as it tells only half the story", and to come up with a proof that uncertainties and variations in electron or quark behaviour can be explained by unequal intensities of the invisible or hidden energy (of the Fire or Light) where the electrons are found. One of our group, who had been a nuclear physicist, undertook to work on this and reactivate Einstein's (and Bohm's) search for a hidden variable. Such an aggressive step forward would, if successful, yank science away from reductionism in one go.

In philosophy, too, there needs to be a revolution as the theories with which philosophers organise science need to be better; one that does not go just one step beyond Wittgenstein and Ayer, one that blows the whistle on Wittgenstein and Ayer and sweeps their disciples out of their positions in the universities. At several meetings of philosophers between October 1991 and June 1992 I called for "bricks to be thrown through certain Oxford and Cambridge college windows, with notes held on by rubber bands calling on the reductionist, logical positivist or linguistic analystic occupiers to resign and make way for philosophers who will get out of the armchair and again see man within our changed universe". This picture unfailingly raises a laugh, or at the very least a smile, but the idea has a point. There is not time for gradualism in philosophy. There must be a sudden and abrupt change so that philosophy can reject linguistic analysis and logical positivism and get back to metaphysical concerns in accordance with the scheme I have outlined in the previous essay (pages 27-8), and therefore necessarily back to the organicism and vitalism of the "process biology" of Whitehead, Bergson and Hulme; one that will include the ontological view of the universe - Truth - as the Fire or Light and derive its epistemology and cosmology from that.

This revolution in science and philosophy, in the metaphysical foundations of science, is often called holism. Holism sees the universe as a physicalist spatial wholeness which includes the observer or scientist and a reality that is not made up of parts. Holism is true as far as it goes, but is not fundamentally different from reductionism; rather it includes a shift in perspective (from the parts to the whole). However, holism says nothing about the Fire or Light.

Universalism differs from holism in that it sees the universal energy of the Fire or Light as being within the microworld and interconnecting all particles, and as flowing into the soul or universal being, creating processes in biology. Universalism, in short, sees the wholeness in terms of the supersensible Fire or Light as the hidden variables Einstein and Bohm have sought. These hidden variables are a consequence of the working of a metaphysical principle (Bohm would say a "hidden dimension" of matter which has implicate order) within the physical universe, and so I have called the revolution in science and philosophy, and in the metaphysical foundations of science, a Metaphysical Revolution. The true antithesis of reductionism is not just a gradual shift in the physicalist, spatial perspective or way of looking (holism), but is a fundamental change to a view of man and the universe as supersensible or metaphysical in terms of the Fire or Light (a point I expressed in a paper to the Cambridge symposium on reductionism of September 1992)[5]. In holism the whole is a quantitative sum of the parts, albeit an undivisible sum. In Universalism the whole is a qualitative spectrum of invisible and visible energies, of metaphysical and physical forces.

The term "metaphysical" suggests "supersensible" or "invisible", the invisible energy (the Fire or Light) which is the reality in the microworld and the hidden variable behind Heisenberg's uncertainty principle. It also suggests a branch of philosophy. The term Metaphysical Revolution therefore has two layers of meaning: the first suggesting a revolution that restores the supersensible or the invisible as the key energy in science; the second suggesting a revolution that restores the branch of philosophy known as metaphysics. This branch of philosophy has four levels (see pages 27-8): ontology, or Reality or Being as the Fire or Light; transpersonal psychology as the study of the centre in the mind (the soul or universal being) where the Light can be contacted; epistemology as knowledge of the Fire or Light through inner meditation, the eye of contemplation;

and cosmology, the view that the cosmos is filled with a hidden supersensible fifth force, cosmological constant and variable which is behind the uncertainty principle and controls mass. At this lowest level of cosmology the concept of a Metaphysical Revolution means an abrupt change from materialism, separatism, mechanism and reductionism to acknowledging a supersensible or invisible reality in the microworld, which, like the atom for 2,500 years, is waiting to be discovered, tested and verified by scientists and whose confirmation will overthrow Heisenberg's uncertainty principle and explain how particles have their mass.

With regard to the Metaphysical Revolution it is sometimes said that revolutions are destructive, like Derrida's deconstruction. The point is that the Metaphysical Revolution is a *counter-revolution*, a return of philosophy and science to where they should be, and the destruction is a cutting down of dead wood that has choked the cultural scene since the healthier days of the Edwardian time. While physics was going through the partial improvement of quantum and relativity theories, philosophy remained firmly reductionist and was involved with logic and language and neglected man's changed place in a changed universe.

Very often the unorthodoxy of one generation becomes the orthodoxy of the next a generation later. The problem for philosophy is to unite the perennial wisdom and science. This involves an integration of consciousness illumined by the Fire or Light, and the reality perceived by science. The problem for scientists is that one's reality changes as one's consciousness expands: when reason sees unity it experiences separateness; when soul feels unity it knows wholeness. The end of philosophy is wisdom which partly involves acknowledging that the esoteric and mystical make just as much sense in terms of one's experience as one's scientific rationality. All aspects of a human being are part of the whole: the reason, the emotions, the intuition, the instincts - and compassion. The image of Plato's charioteer is relevant with the horses as unruly passions under the control of the soul. Today's equivalent would show that in one who has undergone the centre shift from rational, social ego to soul, the four horse-like faculties are under the control of the soul. Reason is therefore not absolute but a useful tool, and intuition cannot be undermined by being equated with the unconscious.

*

Universalism, which brings the soul to a confrontation with the Light, is a movement for Mystic Revival which revives the essence of all religions (whose central idea is the vision of the mystic Light).

The Universalist view of man sees him at both theoretical and practical levels as at one with Nature, the universe and all mankind, through the contemplating soul (Bonaventure's "eye of contemplation" as opposed to the "eye of reason"). The contemplative eye which is known in meditation goes back to medieval mysticism. It draws on the mystical tradition of the Kabbalah, and the English, Flemish, German and Italian medieval mystics who are shown in *The Fire and the Stones*. At the practical level, confronting people with their own contemplative eye and opening them to the Light is a mysticism, a journey along the Mystic Way.

The Mystic Way eventually leads to Truth, as the first Metaphysical poet John Donne said in *Satyre III (On Religion)*:

> "On a huge hill
> Cragged, and steep, Truth stands, and hee that will
> Reach her, about must, and about must goe."

The Mystic Way begins at the bottom of this "huge hill" with awakening to a consciousness of divine Reality (the first stage). Purgation of all that separates us from the One (all our imperfections and illusions) is a long slow haul into the cloud round the top (the second stage). This ends in a measure of detachment from the world of the senses (and so it is sometimes called a Dark Night of Sense). Illumination (the third stage) is when the sun breaks through. It is heady and dazzling and leads to great interest in the sun, our apprehension of the divine. Ecstasy, rapture, introversion and contemplation follow. Then there is a final and more complete purification of the Self, a purification of the spirit (the fourth stage). This is accompanied by a second Dark Night (which is known as the Dark Night of the Soul or Dark Night of the Spirit.) The sun is hidden and the soul ascends through the rarefied atmosphere of the cloud of unknowing that envelops it as all final sense of "I" and personal will ("I want") are eliminated. This phase is experienced as one of confusion, darkness and loss, and even as crucifixion. Finally, there is oneness with the divine Reality: union (the fifth stage). From the peak of the huge hill in union with Truth he can see for miles and enjoy the unitive vision. The seeker is now stable and serene and purely spiritual. The Mystic Way is then seen to be a journey in which the personality is transmuted, so that a seeker has ceased to be an earthly man with an earthly consciousness and has become a heavenly man with a heavenly consciousness. It is now possible for the seeker to have his individuality annhilated and to be reabsorbed in the Infinite, to live within God as in a cloud, to be one with God's transcendent Oneness as well as God's immanence (the sixth and final stage).

The pilgrim on the Mystic Way proceeds by a circuitous, repetitive route. There are many bogs and ditches before the final ascent to the unitive, panoramic view. Like Dante being led by Beatrice up Mount Purgatorio we follow our guide up the Mystic Way until we have transcended and divinised the instinctive, primitive earthly person we began as and are free from our senses and appetites and live in serenity at a high level of contemplative consciousness enfolded in Being.

The Universalist Mystic Way draws on the worldwide tradition of union with the Fire or Light of Reality in all cultures during the last 5,000 years. It is not associated with any one religion. Universalism (in its sense of Universalist religion which according to our fifth opening definition "promotes the Light in the soul of every human being in mankind") is outside all the religions and is common to all of them. It is: the Christian soul's contact with the Light, the Catholic "lumen gentium" and the Orthodox Transfiguration; the Hindu Atman's contact with the Brahman; the Theravadic Buddhist "non-self" ("anatta") and the Mahayan Buddhist universal self's becoming a Buddha (Enlightened One); the Islamic dying away (fana, literally "blowing out") of the individual self to the universal Self which has knowledge of the Light; the Taoist way (Tao) to the Light or Golden Flower; and so it is with other religions, past and present, which I have touched on in Part One of *The Fire and the Stones*. All these encounters with the Light involve a Mystic Way and involve the dying away of the rational, social ego for the universal being or soul where the Light is contacted.

How does Universalism differ from Christianity and other religions? For one thing there is no doctrine in Universalism, just the soul's experience of the Light; so the basic element of contemplative prayer to God is fulfilled in a wordless communion without the mechanical set words of a vicar or priest. For another thing, Universalism is promulgating a message about the Fire or Light which Christianity used to preach but now does not. Universalism has therefore taken on the fundamental role of Christianity and of all the higher religions, whose fundamental message is one about the Fire or Light which can be known by direct experience. Both Christianity and Hinduism have claimed to be universal religions which apply to all mankind, but each has excluded all other religions. Universalism's vision is not of an exclusively Christian or Hindu view of man. As we have just said, it is outside all existing religions. The Universalist goes to the Light for its wisdom and understanding, for the powers of the Universal Intelligence, for healing and for guidance with practical problems which can range from whether a woman can become pregnant to financial crises. The Light acts as an adviser by pouring affirming currents of Light up the spine, and experience has shown that these "answers" to questions are reliable in as much as events happen in accordance with the content of such answers.

Christianity in Western Europe, and consequently in much of Christendom, is in spiritual decay. The Church is more concerned with social issues such as women priests and homosexual clergy (issues that are within the territory of the rational, social ego) than with contacting the Indwelling Light within. Two marginal figures are doing this: Peter Spink, founder of the Omega Order who is also Canon Emeritus at Coventry Cathedral; and Laurence Freeman, prior of the Benedictine Priory of Montreal which was founded from Ealing Abbey in London and which looks back to the Desert Father John Cassian. Both tour the world, teaching, and are spiritual forces. Both have centres. In June 1992 Peter Spink was invited to preach at Chigwell School's Speech Day service in Chigwell church, Essex, and he gave the boys a simple message that you just do not hear in church today: "God is Light". He made the whole school, including its staff, sit and breathe out the Light. Spink does not stress the origin of the Light in the beyond, as Universalism does, preferring to focus on the Indwelling Light within everyone. (I would say the Light is potentially Indwelling within everyone, when the candle of the soul is lit by an influx of Light from beyond.) Spink does not believe in including details of past mystics, nor (as a Christian) in including those from other religions (well over half of mankind): "It is mysticism now that matters and we should stay within our own tradition, which is Christian." In my experience, people like to compare their own experiences to those of Augustine, Hildegard and others, and Universalism differs from the Omega Order in feeling a strong connection with the past mystic tradition - in not feeling that this will put people off - and in focusing on the essence of all religions, the common ground of all religions, so that all mankind on the planet is included, not just one section (Christians).

The Universalist thus relates to the Fire or Light in all cultures and civilisations. In his home civilisation, the European renews the European Fire or Light, and as *The Fire and the Stones* explains, that is the urgent task as present.

Universalism relates to all cultures and civilisations, but it differs from the perennial wisdom. The perennial wisdom or philosophy (as stated for example by Aldous Huxley after a phrase, "philosophia perennis", coined by Leibniz) presents consciousness as a hierarchy of levels, and is largely about everyday people seeking to improve the quality of their lives, which principally involves putting the personal consciousness in touch with the divine Reality which it manifests and reflects so that the higher self can be awakened and play a central part in human life. Universalism reflects this view but adds the disciplined and regular approach to the Light through meditation, the recognition of the vision of the Fire or Light as central to all civilisations, a renewal of the Light in each generation, the involvement of the Light in giving powers and solving problems, and considering all mankind globally in relation to the Light. Universalism adds the dimension of the Fire or Light.

Universalism likewise differs from the New Age. The New Age (a term first used by the Theosophist and devotee of discarnate masters, Alice Bailey) reflects some of the approach of the perennial wisdom; but adds a belief in the powers of the occult. The New Age pays lip service to astrology and the coming Age of Aquarius; to crystals and gems; to spiritual guides, channels, entities and disembodied spirits; to millenarianism; to the occult use of the will. Healing the earth's energy (a practice associated with David Icke, who egocentrically proclaimed himself the son of God) can involve women in opening to the earth and releasing its "male energy" so that it "ejaculates" into their earth goddess-like bodies, and it can involve Neolithic-style rituals at each full moon. As a modern tradition the New Age stresses the sounds and colours of the energy centres, using inner sensing and the sounds emanating from crystals. The use of chanting is allied to clearing and purifying, whereas if we are spirit within the body there is no need to clear in this way. The danger of the New Age approach is that it can become pampering: lonely people having their egos massaged.

New Age cults which emphasise the earth and worldliness are still at the level of purifying the senses (the Dark Night of Sense) rather than at the level of the purified spirit (the Dark Night of Spirit). Those already illumined find they are held back by others who have such an earthly approach - as those who are advanced in the unitive vision find they are held back by those who are still at an early stage on the Mystic Way - while those who are near-beginners of course reject the spiritual view of those who are advanced.

Universalism includes everyone in mankind, at whatever level they are at. All are at some point on the Mystic Way. Universalism is an academic, artistic, philosophical, metaphysical and mystical movement which draws on mysticism, metaphysics and religious experience of God without involving these weirder, occultist or pre-civilisational aspects of what has come to be known as the New Age. Universalism is the New Age cleaned up and related exclusively to the Fire or Light. The mysticism of Universalism is a going forward, a progression; the pre-civilisational sounds are a going backwards, a retrogression.

The philosophy of Universalism is entering all the arts as did Romanticism. Universalist painting, sculpture, music, opera and dance all offer a conception of man in touch with the force of the Light. Novels, poetry and plays are beginning to explore this new conception of man. There will soon be a presentation of Universalist art, a kind of anthology to show what all areas of the new movement have in common. As this new conception of man in the universe spreads, so knowledge has to change, and biology, physics, cosmology, history, philosophy and other academic disciplines are being reinterpreted in the light of the new perceptions of the Universalist outlook. A new literary criticism is ahead to relate man to a living universe in the present and to revalue and reinterpret works of the past which managed to do this.

The new movement of Universalism promises to have all the ferment of movements such as Romanticism and Existentialism at their outset. 1798-9 was an exciting time in Germany and in the British lake district just as Paris was an exciting place to be for the last push of Existentialism after the Second World War under Sartre and Camus. (There was a similar ferment in the occultist Theosophy, which was inspired by channelled messages from ascended masters, but this was a very different kind of movement from Romanticism and Existentialism.) Because the Universalist movement is so new and is breaking new ground in man's consciousness it recalls the movement of psychology in the early part of the 20th century. Freud, Jung, Rank and Adler were all concerned with the subconscious and unconscious minds, but each had their own emphasis. Freud saw the subconscious as a place of neuroses; Jung (who worked with Freud from 1907 to 1912) came to see the collective unconscious as containing health-giving symbols; Rank saw the unconscious as the artist's creative will; and Adler saw it in terms of a will to power. The differing emphases resulted in debate, quarrels and independent work, but as they were all involved in the same quest to understand the subconscious and unconscious minds, we think of them all as being within one movement.

So it is with the Universalist movement and the exploration of consciousness in relation to the Light. There will be differing interpretations of the role of the Light in history and Nature and cosmology, but all who are involved in the same activity will be regarded as belonging to one Universalist movement.

To secure a change in the way science and philosophy are regarded in the universities there must be a movement; otherwise the reductionists (i.e. reductionist scientists and philosophers) will stay in control, will continue to hold the key posts and influence society. To have a movement which can effect an abrupt change means creating an umbrella "ism" (Universalism) with those who support it attempting to convert others who do not take part in the revolutionary battleground of ideas. Isms are labels in a convenient shorthand. Imagine communicating the idea "Romanticism" without the convenient label of the ism. In place of "Romantic art" we would have to use a cumbersome and clumsy phrase like "Art which emphasises feeling and the imagination", yet even then there are layers that are missing. Some prefer to believe that a change will happen anyway whether they take action or not. The concept of a movement worries some, who do not want to be part of a new "ism" or to go out and convert people. Generally the Light counts on human support and it cannot be assumed that inactivity will win the day. Similarly existing groups which may seem sympathetic can in fact be unhelpful: the many issues of *Temenos* for example make no reference to the Fire or Light, stressing the arts of the imagination, even though imagination is defined by Coleridge in terms of the Light; and Actualism - in America Actualist groups imagine (or visualise) the Light instead of regarding it as a real or actual event.

There are always those who belittle the importance of any movement. Some say that "gnosticism" is peripheral to the really cogent issues of our age and that we are irrevocably committed to the path of rational knowledge (i.e. to the path of the rational, social ego). But "gnosis" of the Reality in the microworld and within the quantum universe (the Fire or Light) is the most cogent issue today, and it is simply not true that reason can take us to Truth as such people assert. Some regard all leaders of all movements as obsessive, including leaders of revolutions of thought like Luther, Wordsworth and Coleridge, and Kierkegaard along with leaders of political revolutions such as Lenin, Mao and Gaddafi. It is true that one has to be obsessed to have an original perception and to carry it into action and transform one's civilisation with it, and that the "normal" man with "normal" worldly interests does not ponder on the nature of Reality, and does not carry any idea into action and transform his civilisation. All cultural leaders are inevitably obsessed with a perception or idea that is greater than themselves.

Of movements Whitehead wrote in *Introduction to Mathematics* (1911): "Operations of thought are like cavalry charges in a battle - they are strictly limited in number, they require fresh horses, and must only be made at decisive moments." The decisive moment has arrived to effect a sudden and fundamental change in science and philosophy. The Universalist movement has begun at a decisive moment and its Metaphysical Revolution is its crusading banner.

*

We have dealt with the theoretical side of Universalism as a movement. Theoretical Universalism has created a Metaphysical Revolution in all disciplines. It is now time to look more closely at the practical side, which proclaims Universalism as the essence of all religions and which is creating a practical Mystic Revival at the mystery school I have established in Epping, Essex.

Once there was general instruction in Europe as to how to know the Light through the Christian religion. I have said that until the 17th century the instruction was given from the pulpits of churches and Cathedrals throughout Christendom, and the spire of the church or Cathedral dominated every rural community, village, town or city, and towered above all houses, a finger pointing towards the sun and at the same time a shaft of the Light widening downwards, manifesting into creation. But now the Christian religion has decayed, its central symbolism is forgotten and it no longer puts across its central fundamental message and is racked by doctrinal and social issues: homosexual clergy, women priests, the literalness of the Resurrection. As a result no-one is giving general instruction in how to contact the mystic One.

But first a warning how not to contact it. The universal energy is spiritual, not psychic. It comes from the beyond, from the top down; not from within the body or from the earth, from the bottom up. St Augustine, St Hildegard, St Teresa and many other mystics saw a Light which entered their soul from above. This spiritual view of the Light is the opposite of the psychic view of Tantric Hinduism, which advocates raising the serpentine energy Kundalini from the base of the spine up the subtle body through the psychic centres or chakras to the crown centre, where the psychic opens to the spiritual. This "bottom up" approach begins with the bottom two worlds of the Kabbalah, the physical and psychological, whereas the spiritual "top down" approach begins with the Kabbalah's top two worlds, the divine and spiritual, and draws the divine-spiritual energy of the light down into the psychological and physical, opening the heart.

The mystics who follow the "top down" tradition do not refer to the chakras and look down on the psychic from their higher level. Ken Wilber in his contribution to John White's anthology, *Kundalini, Evolution and Enlightenment*, asks "Are the chakras real?" He concludes that for most mystics of the spiritual tradition, including Sankara and virtually all Ch'an and Zen masters, the knotted chakras have no reality beyond that of mental pictures which enable mystics to picture the flow of energy in specific regions of the body.

There are dangers in pursuing a psychic "bottom up" approach to Kundalini. These can be illustrated by the experience of P, a South American living in England. In October 1991, never having heard of Kundalini yoga, she visited a practitioner of Sahaja yoga who specialises in teaching Kundalini through psychic techniques. There was a partial raising of Kundalini before P was ready, and she experienced - especially during meditation - vibrations (tinglings) in her head, surges of heat and electrical waves, which were unpleasant and interfered with her life. I was asked to provide first aid, to help her recover from her Sahaja mess. P rang me in tears and begged me to help. I met her half an hour later at a friend's house, and after consulting the Light began with simple healing. P felt the heat rush up and out with tremendous force and then cool coming down from my hand. She said she felt a new person. I did a short meditation, and she was calm and peaceful within. I told her, "You've had the operation, now the convalescence." I explained that the physical and psychic heat generated by too early a raising of Kundalini had rushed up and out in a safely conducted way, and that the spiritual and divine coolness had come in and taken its place. In fact there was still more to come out, and P went through a very difficult and traumatic fortnight recovering from what had been unleashed the previous October. The stirred up energies within her seemed to include early childhood memories which were distressing for several months.

At my Epping centre we avoid such dangers by emphasising the "top down" spiritual approach after simple grounding and balancing of the body and psyche. The divine-spiritual Light only enters those who are ready, thus bypassing the dangers of too early a release of psychic Kundalini through yogic exercises on bodies whose psyches are not prepared to withstand the currents that can be released.

The mystery school came into being with an extraordinary effortlessness and inevitability that suggest it has been intended from the invisible world. After a career in education both abroad and in Britain, in 1982 I was asked to take over the school for 3-11 year olds I went to as a boy from 1944 to 1947: Oaklands School in Loughton, Essex. In 1988 I was requested by many new parents coming to the area to found another school and while writing *The Fire and the Stones*, seeing there was no school between Harlow and Loughton and that a new school would be Stansted Airport's local school, I felt moved to look for a site, and after visiting two or three possible houses, found Coopersale Hall, which was the right size, was secluded, and had a splendid Assembly Hall, an orangery-ballroom that had fallen into disrepair and was used for storing picture frames. The Hall was actually then owned by an Oaklands parent, and I applied for planning permission to open a school and acquired the site on faith in November 1988 when the planning permission came through. I had to buy from three separate vendors but miraculously they all sold around the same time and it all got put together.

I had a superb 18th century building on a very ancient site. It was on the old Copt Hall estate and had a tree reputed to have been planted by Elizabeth I in 1568. The house dated from 1776 and there was a 17th century cottage alongside it. At the beginning of the 20th century Coopersale Hall was owned by Lord Lyle, M.P. for Epping, and it was the first home in Epping that Churchill came to in 1924 when he visited Lord Lyle to have discussions which resulted in Churchill's becoming M.P. for Epping. Churchill stayed there during the war.

Almost immediately as if from nowhere 200 names were phoned through to the Oaklands Secretary, and I opened the ground floor in April 1989 to 35 pupils and the upstairs in September 1989 to 150. To do this, enormous changes had to be made. We had to widen the public highway (a condition imposed by the local Council) at a cost of £30,000. We had to double the width of the private drive, which included building an embankment. We had to bring water and gas up the 450 metre road. We had to double the width of the internal drive, which meant fitting large double white gates. We had to install fire screens and fire alarm systems and make several car parks, and we had to build and tarmac a playground with tennis court netting in the inaccessible walled garden. All this I organised myself while writing *The Fire and the Stones*. I found a man with a digger, I bought the gas and water pipes, and it was all done on a shoestring. The septic tank was as large as a submarine and was installed by crane. The local fire brigade provided a fire engine's load of water as it was cemented in. Each time a builder quoted £17,500 for some work on the site we did it ourselves for £2,500, our energy went into the place.

As to the Assembly Hall I put two craftsmen in and told them to get on with pannelling and a year later the work was done. In September 1990 we had 200 children and September 1991 230. Meanwhile during the recession of 1989-1992 I built a four classroom extension, using in-house builders and advising on many of the problems myself. The local M.P. for Epping Forest lived in the 17th century cottage as the school's tenant from September 1989, making it perhaps the only school in the country with its own resident M.P.

All these extraordinary events happened effortlessly, the right people appearing at the right time, and the right financial backing being given at the right time. Then in 1991 the Wrekin Trust collapsed, and it became apparent that something had to be done of a practical nature, and, following interest in *The Fire and the Stones*, in 1992 I opened the mystery school on some Saturdays and Sundays to promote the Light.

If you go to a Zen temple in Japan you receive very little instruction, the onus being on you to find your way yourself. No one tells you to stop thinking; they set you a baffling koan and leave you to ponder over it, without explanation. In Zen, the disciple is not told what to do except to count each breath. Illumination is supposed to arrive by accident, and then it is questioned. Is it a symbol, is reality a darkness behind it? There is an idea in the West that 20 minutes is long enough for a meditation, but that is not enough even to get to the start. In the past the esoteric was guarded and the public were barred. Today the esoteric is becoming exoteric, and clear instruction needs to be given, just as it was from the pulpits in the 17th century up and down the land.

This clear instruction is precisely what we give during the practical sessions at the mystery school. We do not waste time having sessions without instruction. We sit the seekers in a semicircle as Pythagoras did, and tell them very clearly what they are trying to do at the start of each full day or afternoon session. They may be in a group of 20 or as many as 45. I talk to them and explain very clearly that we are moving back from the rational, social ego to the soul. The act of moving back requires discipline and effort - it requires the seekers to get themselves to Epping and to sit on a chair and follow my instructions - but once we have moved beyond language into the silence, then there is no trying, just a surrender and waiting, or in Simone Weil's words, "Waiting on God".

I explain that the bringing down of the Light is safe within a small group. Billy Graham has evangelised in packed football stadia. I couldn't meditate with a football crowd as football yobbos are in no way ready to receive the Light. However, I explain that the Light does not touch the unready; that the first breakthrough into Light only comes to those who are ready. Those drawn to seek out the Foundation of the Light, which can involve driving from as far as Manchester, Bristol or the Isle of Wight, or flying specially from Brussels or Seville, are to some degree already prepared.

We have experimented with the preparatory session. We have tried working to purify the body. We aimed to get to the essence, to purify the heart and the soul and prepare the seekers to open to the Light. This preparatory work was guided and grounded and the body prepared for a safe opening to the Light. The format we are now trying is studying a topic connected with the Light; taking this topic from *The Fire and the Stones*. We are looking at the experience of others in relation to the Light, considering them as models for our long meditation. This leads on to some practical metaphysics. This part of the day is taken by one of our teachers.

After a break we proceed to the meditation, which I lead. The meditation may take 50 minutes, an hour, or even longer: in the Zen temples of Japan there are four meditations of one and a half hours each a day. The Light is a benevolent, good force, contrary to views that it is neutral and depends on the degree of benevolence or malevolence of those using it. The Light is divine and spiritual and comes from the highest levels and it knows who in a group is ready. I guide the meditation with frequent instructions. I say "Thy will, not my will be done", and the Light does leave alone those who are still in their analytical, thinking, rational, social ego, and who cannot cross into their new centre of the soul. Everyone must give themselves permission to move back from the controlling reason and surrender to the unknown.

The form of the meditation is always the same. I take the seekers behind their thoughts, their rational thinking "I" to the "I" behind Descartes' "I think therefore I am". Some want to struggle to clear the confused emotions of the rational, social ego, but I urge them to bypass it completely, simply to go behind it. I urge them to go back across the bridge that leads from their left brain to their right brain, back to the soul. (I say it is "like crossing from north of the Thames to Waterloo", but if the bridge image interferes I urge them just to surrender.) In the course of doing this we leave our bodies behind as it were; we are not aware of our legs and arms, which go to sleep. We move to a place beyond thought, beyond our body - to our soul, which is apart from social mind and body consciousness. We open this like a flower and wait for the Light to pour in. When it has poured in to me I say: "The Light is in this room now. Open to it." I urge them to give themselves permission to surrender to the Light, to let the Light in.

The Light can begin as a speck, a point: Dante's "infinitesimal point". It widens into a hint of a dawn. There are glimmers and gleams. Many see, behind closed eyes, a shaft of Light coming down from above. This top down, divine-spiritual, safe Light descends and enters the body, going down into the lowest centre, and then coming up to light the soul.

WHAT IS UNIVERSALISM?

After inviting everyone to open to the Light I draw attention to the powers of love, wisdom and understanding and invite all to know the love of the Light and to love mankind, to pour out healing energy to all in need. The act of giving energy helps to open the channel that supplies Light, and Light comes in. I use a combination of techniques to persuade the seekers to open to the Light: from pleading with the Light to urging them to give, which opens up the supply channels. I invite all to open to the wisdom of the Light, and I ask all to ask the Light "Why am I here on earth, what is my task, my mission, what is my destiny?" and to listen for the answer. Very often there is an answer that people at a crossroads find helpful. I ask for the powers of understanding of the Light to flow in. Hildegard understood the breviary and the *New Testament* better after knowing the Light, and our seekers say that their reading of books is accompanied by new powers of understanding once they have broken through to the Light.

I draw everyone's attention to the association between the Light and God, and invite all to know God and to feel the inner serenity and peace of the Light. Then I bring them safely out of the Light, folding in the petals of the soul that has opened. Then step by step, very gently, we return from the soul across the bridge to the rational, social ego and then into the body. We reoccupy the body from which we have withdrawn and move our paralysed limbs and open our eyes.

We close the afternoon with a question and answer session. I invite everyone to share what we saw. This session is for interpreting, relating to the tradition, understanding some of the new things that have happened. The centre has a support team, so that there is follow-up after care, and no-one is abandoned. But the question and answer session is crucial. In the course of this I always say that we have experienced the essence of all religion: what the early Christian disciples experienced in the catacombs, and the essence of Hinduism and Buddhism. Any residual impurities get forced down, and it is not uncommon at our

89

meditations for seekers who are opened to the Light to have swollen fingers. The swellings soon go down, and the ecstasy felt by those opened can last two or three days and amply compensates for the inconvenience. Once a pathway has been opened there is no reason why the Light should not come through each time in meditation. So one woman who opened on a Saturday, opened again the following Wednesday and again the following Sunday, and again the next time we meditated, and sat in a blissful trance at the end of each meditation, virtually unable to move.

It sometimes happens that a powerful experience of the Light can prevent someone from functioning properly for a few days. This should not be cause for worry. Any transformational move from the rational, social ego (the normal functioning centre which deals with one's bank manager and employer) to a new centre in the soul has the effect of making a person malfunction for a while. In fact, to live from a new centre is highly confusing at first.

Too early an experience of the Light can lead to its recipient becoming too self-preoccupied, blind to others, self-absorbed and (like the Quietist Mme Guyon) too ready to sit in a trance and neglect practical everyday tasks which have to be done. This is a temporary phase. For by the time the recipient is in the unitive phase he or she is doubly alert to others.

The day closes with social chatter over tea. During this time certain individuals discuss when they may be ready to have their own groups. As I said at our first meeting, if 10 out of 45 go off to different parts of Britain and start their own weekly groups at home, then there is a national movement. And this is precisely what has happened with Universalism. There are groups of 10 within Britain and in Europe and across the world, and these are shortly to be linked by a Journal. How they are kept in touch without the message being diluted is another problem, for which we are considering a solution.

What we have done is to practise the essence of all religions. *The Fire and the Stones* shows how all religions have the Fire or Light in common, and by inviting an experience of the Light we are in the centre of all religions, as it were. All present in our centre relate their experience to that of all mankind and all mystics in all civilisations, and those who have taken part can then go back into their own religion if they wish, and practise it within a Christian, Hindu or Buddhist context, or elsewhere. Or they can keep the practice outside all religions, denominations and sects as a Universalist practice, in which case they are at the early stage of a Universalist network and of a Mystic Revival outside all religions. To the extent that the experience is an individual one, it is an existential (or rather, post-Existential) contact with metaphysical Reality, the mystic One. To the extent that it is a social experience, the group renews its civilisation. To the extent that is global, the group connects with all other groups in the world, which form a Universalist network. To the extent that it is a cosmic experience, the group is bringing down and tapping into the central energy of the universe, the reality in the microworld which has immense power. At present it seems that this energy is metaphysical - beyond physics. In fact it may manifest on the electromagnetic spectrum, at a very high frequency, up at the gamma end. In the next century its manifestation may appear on the electromagnetic spectrum and be within the territory of physics.

I have spelt out what happens at our mystery school meetings, where future Ambassadors of the Light come forward or reveal themselves by sharing their gifts, to demystify something secret and hidden and to make our format wider known.

We are now introducing a study-and-meditation theme. We plan to put on a course on Universalism, when we will focus on the soul's contact with Light in each particular religion before going on to practical meditation. We intend to put on a course on mysticism, when we will focus on the soul's contact with the Light in different mystics before going on to practical meditation. We intend to put on a course on the Metaphysical Revolution where we will focus on the Light's presence in different disciplines (such as biology, physics and philosophy) before going on to practical meditation. This study-and-meditation approach widens the practical educational approach of the mystery school.

Our practical sessions are bringing about a Mystic Revival in our time just as our theoretical arguments are working towards a Metaphysical Revolution. Universalism sees each man, woman and child in the world, black or white, rich or poor, hungry or fed, as a soul who is swept with tides of Light and who is in a reciprocal, dynamic relationship with a vital, loving universe. It is committed to a way of action to spread this view, with its corollary that "all mankind is my brother".

Every genuine revival has its own emphasis. The 16th century Protestant Reformation emphasised justification by faith. The 17th century Puritan movement emphasised the sovereigny of God. The 18th century Wesleyan Revival emphasised a new birth through the heart. The 19th century Evangelical Awakening emphasised world evangelism. The 20th century Universalist Revival emphasises the common ground between all world religions in terms of the Fire or Light, and is creating a global network of inter-religious groups. Our Mystic Revival therefore goes a step beyond all the previous recent genuine revivals as it widens the area targeted from Christendom to what Christendom has in common with other religions, and therefore to all mankind.

To sum up, Universalism is a post-Existentialist philosophy that sees man in relation to the metaphysical ontological reality of the One Fire or Light which manifests down into spiritual psychology, epistemology and cosmology. Its progress in philosophy and science is linked to the fortunes of an anti-reductionist Metaphysical Revolution, which seeks to bring about an abrupt change in both philosophy and science. At a practical level Universalism is associated with a Mystic Revival and, as the soul's encounter with the Light of Being, it epitomises the essence of all religions and has a new emphasis on the common ground between all world religions. Universalism proclaims the common basis of humanity where, irrespective of education, wealth or race, and the particularities of body and mind, the soul is filled with the Light. Universalism proclaims what all mankind has in common in relation to eternity as well as time: the peaceful Light which is a basis for world peace.

A new view of man and the universe, a new Mystic Revival, a new Metaphysical Revolution, a new post-Existentialist philosophy and a new essential religion and international movement - to experience all these aspects of Universalism, come and join us in Epping[6] at one of our openings to the Fire or Light.

Notes

1. See pages 9-12 and Appendix for Universalist history.
2. Quoted in Ken Wilber's *Eye before Eye*, p3.
3. Hawking made his remark about the Big Crunch in my presence at a Science Evening at Logan Hall, London on 30th April 1992.
4. I am indebted to the philosopher Geoffrey Read for information in this paragraph.
5. See pages 95-120 for this paper.
6. To make contact, write to the Foundation of the Light, c/o 24 Beresford Road, North Chingford, London E4 6EE (tel: 081-529-8097). Heather Andrews Dobbs of this address has also published *New Light*, the Journal of the Thomas Troward Society, which is also available from this address.

REDUCTIONISM, HOLISM AND UNIVERSALISM: METAPHYSICAL SCIENCE AND THE METAPHYSICAL REVOLUTION

(Argument: The true antithesis of reductionism is not physicalist holism but metaphysical Universalism, whose whole has a non-physical source outside Nature; and the metaphysical approach creates a metaphysical science, the "much-desired union of science and metaphysics" that Bergson called for, which has launched a Metaphysical Revolution that challenges materialism, mechanism and reductionism in all the sciences and philosophy.)

Reductionism in philosophy holds that entities (or any things that exist) of a particular kind are collections or combinations of entities of a simpler or more basic kind; and that expressions regarding such entities can be defined in terms of expressions regarding more basic entities. Reductionism in the physical sciences dissects a system into many simple units and describes a complex structure in terms of the laws governing its components.

Biological and mental events were reduced to physical events in the mechanistic and deterministic 19th century philosophy of the Darwinist biologist T.H. Huxley. In the 20th century, reductionist physicists have used classical physics to reduce the universe to granular atoms (atomism). Biological and medical reductionists have reduced the human body to a collection of atoms and chemically controlled cells. Reductionist geneticists have reduced man to a collection of genes. Reductionist brain physiologists and psychologists have reduced the mind to physiological brain functions. Analytic and linguistic philosophers have analysed concepts and language and have reduced all existing things and all states of affairs to observable objects or sense data, and all statements of fact to empirically verifiable statements. They have reduced all statements to collections of thoughts or words, which are then examined for meaning, and any non-empirically verifiable statements are held to be meaningless, including statements about mystical experience. Man's expressions of his highest religious aspirations have thus been reduced to the status of meaningless questions.

Reductionism fits in with the unified science of materialistic physicalism (which asserts that the only reality is the physical world), and some reductionists argue that the theoretical entities of all sciences can be reduced to those of a more basic science: physics. Chemistry can be reduced to physics because there is a quantum mechanical theory of the chemical bond. Biology is an application of physics and chemistry to the dynamic structures of natural history, whose molecules are continuously replaced; molecular biology reduces organisms to complicated physical systems. Physiology can be reduced to the terms of physics and chemistry. Scientific psychology can be reduced to neurophysiology and cybernetics, and ultimately to physics. Consciousness does not fit in as mental events are not the sum of physical events. In psychology, however, the behaviourism of Watson and B. F. Skinner has reduced consciousness to physical behaviour, and central state theorists have reduced mental states to states within the body, while there has been an attempt at a new materialism or physicalism by analytic philosophers who have sought to reduce mental events to physical states and events in terms of the electrical discharges in the brain.

Reductionism assumes (1) that the universe is granular and materialistic; (2) that the universe is mechanistic, like a machine with cogs; (3) that the objective phenomenal world alone is real; (4) that its reality can be apprehended by positivist observation and sense data; and (5) that the scientist is separate from the world he is studying. Reductionism is materialistic, mechanistic, objectivist, positivist and separatist.

19th century science was based on observation, sense data, experiment and testing. 20th century science has involved mathematics, which have undermined the traditional science. Reductionism is associated with classical physics and has been undermined by the mathematics of the relativity and quantum theories. The 19th century granular world of matter has been replaced by a sea of energies in which light can be both particles and waves and the electrons of matter have uncertain positions and are best seen as events in a process, behaving in seemingly random and indeterminate ways in accordance with Heisenberg's uncertainty principle. The objective phenomenal world is subject to real underlying quantum forces, and observation and sense data are now subject to mathematics. The relativity and quantum theories show that the observer is a relational part of the universe he is observing. Mechanistic reductionism has been undermined from within science itself.

Reductionism has worked well for 300 years and is responsible for the advance in knowledge and technology of modern science. It was natural to seek to understand the processes of Nature, minds and bodies by looking at their very small components. However, this method, which has in the past yielded good results, has ceased to be effective today, as science itself has discovered that reality is more than the sum of particles and subparticles.

*

What is taking the place of reductionism? The antithesis of reductionism has been held to be holism. Holism in philosophy holds that entities can only be understood in relation to the whole, which comprises a hierarchy of irreducible wholes. The whole is understood spatially, suggesting "all of the universe" or "all of the body" or whatever whole is being referred to at any time.

Goethe (and later Rudolf Steiner) proposed a science of wholes, but holism itself is a 1920s idea that originated with a perception in biology by the South African philosopher Jan Smuts (Prime Minister of South Africa from 1939 to 1948), who said in *Holism and Evolution* (1926) that everywhere we look at Nature we see wholes, and not just

97

simple wholes but hierarchical wholes: whole fields within whole fields at ascending levels. Smuts held that the universe is not static but dynamic, and produces ever higher and higher level wholes which are ever more organised. Evolution is the drive to every higher unities, which Smuts called holism.[1]

Anti-reductionist biologists have held that molecular biology cannot explain all aspects of living forms. Vitalists such as the German Driesch (a convinced vitalist by 1895), the French Bergson (*Creative Evolution*, 1907) and du Noüy proposed a vital entity or impulse in all living things, an intrisic factor that activates life. Nature has come to be regarded as an organic process which includes the observer, as in Whitehead's "philosophy of organism" in *Process and Reality* (delivered as lectures 1927-8, published 1929). Organicists who derived from Whitehead's "philosophy of organism", such as Ludwig von Bertalanffy and Edward Stuart Russell, have claimed that organisms must be interpreted as functioning wholes. Whitehead held that there is a definite property of wholeness that enables organisms to develop, and Russell wrote in *The Interpretation of Development and Heredity* (1930): "In our conception of the organism we must...take account of the unifiedness and wholeness of its activities....Organismal biology attempts to study the actual modes of action of whole organisms, regarded as conditioned by, but irreducible to, the modes of action of lower unities."

The holistic view of living organisms holds that they have emergent properties that cannot be predicted by their physics and chemistry (e.g. plant tropisms and animal instincts); and that there is a wholeness in the scheme of evolution and animal processes. The holistic view of organisms holds that irreducible wholes are the determining factor in biology, and control-and-regulation mechanisms operating at molecular level make these organism systems in effect sophisticated kinds of cybernetic or automatic-control systems which follow self-determining and self-organising principles.

Holism is therefore similar to reductionism in seeing organisation in terms of cybernetics.

Holism has been widened from biology and evolution to physics, psychology and other sciences, and it has had some effect on these contemporary sciences. In physics there is now a greater emphasis on the whole, and David Bohm suggested in *Wholeness and the Implicate Order* (1980) that there is an underlying whole order beneath the apparent chaos and randomness of physics, an unmeasurable and undetectable order behind the energy and mass of physics which Bohm describes as a "hidden dimension" but which he has said elsewhere is matter, not mental consciousness. Bohm proposed a hidden variability in the microworld which explains the uncertainty principle. In the anti-atomistic Gestalt psychology, which was founded by Wertheimer in 1912, attention has been paid to minds as wholes. The American neurobiologist (or psychobiologist) Roger Sperry, whose work on cerebral hemispheres in the 1940s has made possible a map of mental processes, has written (1987) of "downward causation" regarding hierarchical wholes in which "things are controlled not only from below upward but also from above downward by mental, social, political, and other macro properties" and "primacy is given to the higher level controls rather than the lowest" (an idea which Sperry has hailed as a "consciousness revolution in science" and which Popper has described as "a new view of evolution").[2] In holistic medicine the whole health of the patient is taken into account, including the patient's state of mind, not just the limb or part being treated. In genetics there is a move to see the genes in relation to man as a whole.

Holism has a mainly theoretical basis. It is a way of looking, without many tangible results at the level of verification, testing, scientific experiment, observation or sense data. David Bohm's hidden variables and Rupert Sheldrake's morphogenetic fields (Sheldrake has proposed a vitalist theory of morphic resonance) have not been proved, yet, and can therefore be deemed by reductionists to be speculative. The view of Nature as process, self-determining organisation and hierarchical wholes are all to some extent at the level of hypothesis or philosophical perspective (such as Whitehead's) and the neo-Darwinian view remains strong in scientists such as Richard Dawkins, who rejects teleology. There is no conclusive rational argument for holism, no mathematical equation and no positive experience of the whole, which Bohm asserts is unmeasurable and spatially infinite, and which therefore by definition cannot be experienced by our finite minds. Holism is at heart an insight. There are many perceptions which suggest that the whole is present in the part (the whole tree in the seed, for example) and there is much sound imagination, but in the last analysis holism remains a theory.

Holistic theories opposed to mechanistic reductionism hold that as the complexity of living systems increases, new properties emerge which are more than the sum of the systems' parts. Some holistic thinkers (such as Gregory Bateson) see these new properties as being potentialities within matter, and they are in effect sophisticated materialists or physicalists who deny survival after death. Non-materialist holistic thinkers (such as Rupert Sheldrake) see the order, purposiveness and creativity of organisms as being dependent on a non-physical source which is beyond the natural world, such as a divine principle which is both beyond and in Nature, both transcendent and immanent. Parts of organisms are held to have a teleological purpose in relation to the whole, and some holists say life itself is purposive; which raises the question of whether a biological system can have a goal that is similar to a human goal within the equivalent of a divine plan.

We need to distinguish two quite separate holisms. There is physicalist, materialist holism which sees the whole as immeasurable and perhaps infinite, but essentially spatial and non-transcendental; a whole in which organisms move towards new wholes like cybernetic machines, either through material, physical fields or through human thought or through a consciousness immanent within Nature, within a creative, self-organising universe. Then there is a metaphysical, transcendental holism whose whole (perhaps like Bohm's "hidden dimension") operates outside physicalist laws because it manifests from the beyond from a metaphysical Reality outside Nature, which transcends Nature; a whole in which organisms move towards wholes with an organising force and teleological purpose, and relate to a whole life which is within an overall metaphysical teleological whole.

Holism was originally advanced by Smuts in the first, physicalist sense, as the reverse of an obverse reductionism. The term "holism" should therefore be confined to this physicalist sense, and holism is essentially about whole fields as opposed to fragmented parts of those fields, which the reductionist sees (and undermines hierarchies by reducing them to one level). Holism in relation to reductionism is little more than a change of perspective, a change of a way of looking. Instead of seeing the whole as a collection or combination of parts, to whose sum it can be reduced, it sees an irreducible whole which is organicist but still fully explicable by science. Holism emphasises the whole universe, the whole human being, the whole body, but the whole universe is still a universe that can be completely investigated by physics and biology and other sciences. The whole human being may include spiritual and paranormal faculties, and the whole body may include subtle energies, but these too can be completely investigated by science. (There is arguably a hierarchical system of knowledge as ascending wholes from the physical sciences to the life sciences to the human sciences and to the spiritual sciences.) Reductionism and holism represent different ways of looking at the universe of the sciences, but the difference is quantitative rather than qualitative.

The second, metaphysical holism, which includes the first, physicalist holism, originates outside the physical world and Nature and manifests downwards (cf Sperry), and is qualitatively different from the first holism in view of its metaphysical source. In the interests of clarity it needs to be called something other than holism. For this second holism I have already proposed the term "Universalism".[3]

*

"Universalism" suggests a universal, metaphysical whole or all with a universal energy which flows into the universal being of organisms with great universality, an organising force that manifests from beyond Nature into Nature and drives them forward into ever higher unities towards a universal, non-physical purpose. In its practical applications, such a manifesting universal energy could be testable. But before we consider the practical empirical implications we need to consider such a metaphysical view from rational and intuitional points of view.

Metaphysics is a puzzle to the man in the street because there is no clear definition and a lack of available instruction. Definitions that are often put forward include the reference by early students of Aristotle to "ta meta ta phusika", what comes "after" physics, i.e. the subject dealt with chronologically after the subject of physics. Metaphysics (which Aristotle himself called "first philosophy") is "the study of the first principles of things, including such concepts as being, substance, essence, time, space, cause, identity etc." or "the ultimate science of Being and Knowing" (OED). From this concern with ontology metaphysics has come to be regarded as what is "beyond" physics ("the science of things transcending what is physical or natural", OED, i.e. what is beyond physicalism, the supersensible); or what is "behind" or "hidden within" physics[4]: the study of Being or Reality, or "the study of the first principles of Nature and Thought" (Chambers' *20th Century Dictionary*). Metaphysics is also a branch of philosophy which studies Being or Reality.

In fact, approached rationally, metaphysics is the science of a universal whole or all, and refers to every possible concept of the mind; not to every existing concept but to every possible concept. This includes all things abstract or concrete, natural or supernatural, known or unknown, and probable or improbable.

Metaphysics is a universal science and deals with laws, common to all, and the structure of all. The most fundamental concept of metaphysics is the idea that encompasses a universal all. This idea is infinity, in an infinite number of dimensions including those we know, i.e. infinite space (endless space without beginning or end) and infinite time (eternity without beginning or end).[5]

The outlook of metaphysics as every possible concept has led to the following rational scheme, which reflects the four hierarchical levels and worlds of the Kabbalah and which is reflected in Guénon's *The Multiple States of Being*[6]:

Infinity: the One, Supreme Being, transcendent non-duality, universal possibility, every possible concept;

Non-Being: manifestation of infinity, metaphysical zero which includes all potentialities of Being and everything unmanifested;

Being: manifestation of Non-Being, which contains everything manifested and envelops Existence and contains all possibilities of Existence;

Existence: manifestation of Being, multiplicity which is contained in the unity of Being.

From Existence upwards each level is a hierarchy of ascending wholes, each of which is included in the one above. Thus Existence is included in Being, which is included in Non-Being, which is included in Infinity or Supreme Being. Conversely, as we shall see (p107), manifestation is a "downward" process from Infinity or the One, through the void or quantum vacuum of Non-Being into the unity of Being and then the diversity and multiplicity of Existence.

According to Whitehead, speculative philosophy (he means metaphysics) is "the endeavour to frame a coherent, logical, necessary system of general ideas in terms of which every element of our experience can be interpreted" (*Process and Reality*, 1929). Physicalist holism does not seek to supply a system of general ideas which covers every element of our experience and every possible concept including universal categories and hierarchical wholes outside Nature. It emphasises a perspective of whole fields within whole fields at successive levels within Nature, a totality of spatial fields which is never static or complete but in an unending process of movement, and in terms of the above scheme these fields are at the physical level of Existence. The universal all of metaphysical Universalism is more all-embracing as it is the totality of all possible concepts and hierarchical wholes, including those outside Nature, and therefore of all the above levels: Infinity, Non-Being, Being and Existence. It is multi-level - it applies to four levels and incorporates all known levels within its whole - and is more total than the spatial, physicalist, holistic whole which is mono-level. Thus reductionism is included in physicalist holism (whose whole includes reductionist parts), which is in turn included within metaphysical Universalism - in a hierarchy of ascending wholes, each of which is included in the one above.

Such a rational, logical, metaphysical scheme is reinforced by the intuitional, contemplative, existential or mystical approach. Our intuitions are part of our experience, and we are not reason alone, but also instincts, feelings and intuitions. All aspects of man must be included in the universal whole of the metaphysical scheme. There are rational and empirical aspects to Whitehead's endeavour to frame a system of general ideas which interprets all experience, and in so far as the reason is used, it is used as a tool, the approach being contemplative, not rational.

It is important to grasp that through contemplation our intuitive vision can see the infinite, divine One or Supreme Being of the metaphysical Reality. As we are part of the oneness of the whole, and are not separate from it, we can contact this Reality by inner knowing. Even though our reason is finite and the Universalist whole is infinite, the divine part of ourselves, the universal being or soul which is part of the infinite whole, can receive the mystic and metaphysical Reality in an experience which is central to all the religions. In *The Fire and the Stones*[7] I have traced a 5,000 year old tradition of Being as metaphysical Fire - the cosmic Fire of Heracleitus - which according to the tradition is behind the stuff of creation at the cosmological level but which can be known epistemologically through gnosis of the mystical vision of the ontological One Fire or Light (the Light known to St Augustine, Gregory the Great and St Bernard, and many other mystics). There is no space here to give a full treatment of this mystical vision. I have dealt with it fully in *The Fire and the Stones*, which gives hundreds of experiences during the last 5,000 years.

St Bonaventure, the 13th century mystic, distinguishes the "eye of the flesh" - the eye of scientific observation and empirical sense impressions - from the "eye of reason", which sees philosophical categories and organises sense data, and the "eye of contemplation" or the higher intellect, which sees the metaphysical and mystical Reality. Kant pointed out that the reason, by its very nature, cannot approach the metaphysical Reality, which is beyond reason (the reason cannot see into heaven); and that if it attempts to do so it confuses categories. He did not go on to say that metaphysical Reality can only be approached by the "eye of contemplation", and as a result of Kant the rational approach to metaphysics came to be dismissed as speculative and fell into disrepute, metaphysics being understood in a derogatory sense of extravagant system-building, while the contemplative approach to metaphysics fell into disuse.

Traditional science eschews contemplation, preferring experiments, observation and sense data, and recently mathematics. Progressive scientists are now revising and extending their view of what is admissible, and are acknowledging that, as we are not separate from the objective world but are part of the oneness, we can contact reality not just through our senses but through deep intuitive inner knowing. Such scientists are acknowledging that consensual self-reports of inner experience are as valid as objective data, and some have concluded that the highest form of knowledge is not empirical knowledge via the senses, but gnosis: the contemplative perception of the Reality behind the phenomenal world. Whitehead expressed this point of view at the end of *Modes of Thought* (1938, from an address to Harvard in 1935): "The purpose of philosophy is to rationalize mysticism."

According to the metaphysical tradition, which draws on the perennial wisdom, the Fire or Light is the reality (compare Plato's fire in the cave) and the phenomenal world is its shadows. Universalism proposes that the reality in the microworld is the metaphysical Fire or Light, an invisible energy which through different intensities causes electrons to react differently in different localities and therefore accounts for the uncertainty principle; that it also acts as an expanding force which counteracts gravity (the expanding force Newton sought unsuccessfully), and as Einstein's cosmological constant; and that it, rather than Higgs's particle, is responsible for the origin of mass and therefore gives the universe the form it does. Universalism proposes that the manifested form of this invisible principle of the Fire or Light may be on the electromagnetic spectrum, beyond natural light (whose individual rays are invisible) and beyond gamma rays, at the high frequency end of the spectrum.[8]

Metaphysics, as a branch of philosophy, has four subdivisions, which correspond to the four different hierarchical levels of our rational scheme (see page 103):

ontology: i.e. Supreme Being or Reality, the transcendent and immanent Fire or Light, the infinite One;

transpersonal or spiritual psychology: focus on the part of the self (the universal being or soul) beyond the rational social ego where Reality is known;

epistemology: how Reality is known in relation to the human mind, the need for a transformational centre shift from the ego to the soul;

cosmology: the world of physics where any invisible reality that cannot be tested is deemed speculative.

These four subdivisions of metaphysics in turn reflect the four different hierarchical levels through which (according to the tradition) Being manifests "downward" into physical, cosmological form:

real nothing: transcendent Reality, Supreme Being, or the Fire or Light, before it became immanent;

Non-Being: the quantum vacuum, which contains all potentialities of Being;

Being: all the potentialities of Existence within the Fire or Light, the invisible immeasurable but experienceable reality or immanent Being within the microworld;

Existence: the visible, measurable world of cosmology and physics.

On this view, the metaphysical Fire is the One Reality of ontology, which manifests into the quantum vacuum, is associated with symbols and the collective unconscious, and contains the potentialities of Being. It then manifests into Being which contains the potentialities of Existence, all subatomic particle seeds and morphogenetic germs, the power behind Nature which the Romantic poets sensed epistemologically. It then manifests into Existence, the visible Nature of our phenomenal world with all its diversity and particularities.

When seen in relation to metaphysics, the true antithesis of reductionism is not physicalist holism, which is a huge physical energy dimension but has no metaphysical dimension; but Universalism, a philosophy that focuses on the universal energy of the metaphysical Fire or Light which permeates all four levels of the whole and the universe, which comes into the universal being or soul or essence behind the rational, social ego, and which has been known by the mystics and can potentially be known - experienced - by all mankind with great universality. Universalism is a post-Existentialist philosophy which emphasises the unity of Being rather than the diversity of Existence, and the interconnected contemplative soul rather than the separate rational, social ego: the unified, interconnected "I" behind the Descartes' separate "I think therefore I am", in which the "I" that is doing the thinking is the Cartesian rational, social ego, not the contemplating soul. In such a metaphysical model of the universe, man is like a sponge in a quantum sea of Being.

Universalism differs from physicalist holism in that it focuses on the metaphysical Reality of the Fire or Light. Universalism sees the whole as being permeated by the metaphysical Fire or Light - and it proposes that there could be no whole without the controlling Fire or Light which holds it all together, which governs electron behaviour, balances gravity, creates order and controls mass as the principle that is behind the uncertainty principle, the cosmological constant, implicate order and Dark Matter. The eye of contemplation in the contemplative soul, as opposed to the eye of reason, can see this whole at work when it gazes in contemplation on the mystic Light.

A Universalist paradigm answers the main criticism made against the holistic paradigm, that it confuses categories, by mixing physics and mysticism; physicalism and the metaphysical. Physicists have become interested in Eastern mysticism and metaphysics. Wheeler has said, "No theory of physics that deals only with physics will ever explain physics," and Sarfatti has said, "Meta-physical statements are absolutely vital for the evolution of physics," recalling Einstein's "anyone who studies physics long enough, is inevitably led to metaphysics". Absolute Spirit, the highest state of Being which is both transcendent and immanent, has been confused with the physicalist whole in physics, biology and psychology, the shadows in Plato's cave with "the Light beyond the cave"(Wilber). Wilber describes this confusion as pantheistic reductionism[9], as the Reality of metaphysics is of a different level of Being from that of physicalist holism.

If we go beyond physicalist holism, however, to metaphysical Universalism, then there is no confusion of categories or reductionism, for the metaphysical Reality - the Light, as Wilber calls it - manifests into the physical world of Nature as a universal metaphysical energy which is an invisible reality in the microworld. There are many instances of this manifestation in *The Fire and the Stones*, which answers Wilber's worries on the relationship between physics and mysticism. A metaphysical Universalist paradigm avoids the confusions of the physicalist, holistic paradigm, and unites metaphysics and science.

*

Bergson (in his *Introduction to Metaphysics*, 1903) called for "a much-desired union of science and metaphysics, properly so-called, to become conscious of their true scope, often far greater than they imagine". Such a union would in fact be a reunion, for the founders of the Royal Society (founded in 1660) such as Boyle, Wren, Moray and Newton were steeped in the esoteric, metaphysical traditions of Freemasonry, Rosicrucianism, Neoplatonism and Hermeticism (which I have reflected in *The Fire and the Stones*).[10] Bergson (not to mention Whitehead) would have been extremely interested in our metaphysical paradigm.

Metaphysical science is science that connects to every possible concept, not just to every existing concept, and which therefore relates to Infinity and a source beyond the physicalist world of Nature (which rational, materialistic physicalists describe as speculative). It is science which relates to an intuitional approach to Reality as we are part of the oneness, not separate from it, and can contact reality through inner knowing as well as through sense data.

Metaphysics relates the universe to ultimate principles, and so therefore does metaphysical science.

The foundations of modern science have an ontology. As Willis Harman claims in *Global Mind Change*, there are three differing foundations or bases of science: materialistic monism (that mind comes from matter); dualism (that mind and matter are separate, the position of Sir John Eccles); and transcendental monism (that matter comes from mind).[11] To these should be added metaphysical non-duality, that both mind and matter manifest from the metaphysical Reality of the one Fire or Light, and are one within the overall four-level scheme; and that there is diversity in the phenomenal world as well as unity behind it at the level of Being and ultimately at the level of the One. (Strictly, monism does not allow for diversity as well as unity.) Many scientists are now of the opinion that transcendental monism accords best with their wholeness view of the universe of which they are part, but for some, metaphysical non-duality will accord best with their metaphysical view of the universe.

The foundations of most modern (objectivist, positivist and reductionist) science have a materialist ontology in terms of the phenomenal world (which it sees as the only reality) with the scientist separate from the world he describes; and an epistemology as sense data, and more recently mathematics. The foundations of the new holistic science have a wholeness ontology in terms of physicalist wholeness, oneness, interconnectedness, with the scientist an indivisible part of the wholeness he describes; and an alternative epistemology of inner knowing of the oneness we are part of along with sense data, as we encounter reality not just through our physical senses but also through our intuitive, spiritual, mystical sense. The foundations of a new metaphysical science have a metaphysical ontology of the mystic and metaphysical Fire or Light or Supreme Being which manifests through four levels into the physical world and organises living forms and controls the universe, with the scientist a part of a manifesting Reality; and an alternative epistemology as contemplative gnosis of the mystic and metaphysical Fire or Light, which is also known as God, the intuitional Reality which controls the microworld.[12] Metaphysical science is science with an ontology and epistemology that are quite different from those of reductionist and holistic science.

A metaphysical science will question and challenge reductionism in the sciences and philosophy, and will develop physicalist holism into a metaphysical Universalist position. It will carry the Metaphysical Revolution into many areas of science and philosophy, and will have much to propose on the workings of the manifesting metaphysical Reality (ontology) in the universe (cosmology). It has many practical empirical implications. More specifically, metaphysical science will research and test and do mathematics on the following ten hypotheses:

1. Origin of the universe: seeing the hot beginning (Big Bang) in relation to the metaphysical reality of the Fire or Light.

2. Reality in the microworld: seeing the metaphysical reality of the Fire or Light as Newton's expanding force (or fifth force), Einstein's cosmological constant, the principle of hidden variability, and the origin of mass, all of which are effects of its invisible varying intensities in different localities.

3. Electromagnetic spectrum: locating the metaphysical reality of the manifesting Light at the high frequency, gamma end of the spectrum.

4. Brain physiology: seeing consciousness as a system of high frequency light which connects to all rays on the electromagnetic spectrum in the region of 4 cycles per second; measuring responses at this frequency to establish the gateway to global consciousness.

5. Mind-body problem: seeing the mind (and consciousness) as a Bose-Einstein syndrome, as photons that are not dependent on physiological processes but which use the brain for their own metaphysical purposes; seeing the mind as independent of the body.

6. Synchronicity: seeing synchronicity or coincidences as evidence of a unified interconnectedness of matter and consciousness.
7. Mysticism: seeing religious experiences and mystical states of consciousness as contact with the mystic and metaphysical Reality that manifests into and pervades the universe, pouring its universal energy (the Fire or Light) into the universal being or souls of humans.
8. Universalism: seeing the Absolute Infinity as the mystic and metaphysical Reality which can be known intuitionally or existentially through contemplation.
9. Evolution: seeing all evolution in terms of the teleological evolutionary power of the Fire or Light.
10. Philosophy: seeing metaphysical or speculative (Whitehead's word) philosophy as framing a system of general ideas that includes all the above possible concepts; philosophy returning to Whitehead's aims after a lean time and focusing on the whole universe at all hierarchical levels and on life as a whole.

Metaphysical science thus penetrates into many areas of physics, biology, physiology, psychology and other related sciences, and there is so much urgent work to do that a Chair in Metaphysical Science should immediately be set up in a prominent university such as Cambridge to get the Metaphysical Revolution under way.

Out of such work can come a truly universal Theory of Everything, a TOE that includes all levels and all possible concepts, and not just one level. For if the universe is seen in terms of the metaphysical Fire or Light, then it is seen to be a living organic thing rather than a dead thing. Its tidal forces can be seen to flow into all living things, and it is perceived by many to be a universe filled with energies of wisdom, understanding, healing and thought, which flow in from a Universal Mind or Universal Intelligence, which can guide our lives. A Theory of Everything must include these powers which mystics know can flow into the deeper mind, and which poets know can bring symbols into the soul. It is legitimate to ask of any scientific Theory of Everything,

"Where in your theory are love and prayer?" For if they are omitted the theory is incomplete and is a partial theory, not a theory of everything. If the universe is seen in terms of the metaphysical Fire or Light, then a Theory of Everything becomes possible which includes such powers and the spiritual insights of religion, mysticism and metaphysics, as well as the findings of the physical sciences and true philosophy. History is integrated in this total vision: in *The Fire and the Stones* (which is subtitled *A Grand Unified Theory of World History and Religion*) I have demonstrated that the metaphysical Fire or Light is the central vision of 25 civilisations, which grow when the vision is strong and decline when the vision weakens and turns secular. (This is metaphysical history whereas Toynbee's *A Study of History* is holistic history, with a sense of history as a physicalist whole and an awareness of spirituality, but not metaphysical history because he does not see the metaphysical Fire or Light as the central idea of all civilisations.)

There is a feeling that in theoretical physics ideas must be testable if they are to be taken seriously, yet theoretical speculation has outpaced experiment, and ideas have been accepted that cannot be tested. Inflationary theory, for example, may not be testable, and therefore may be metaphysics rather than physics even though it features in all contemporary books on cosmology and the physical universe. In the same way there is a feeling that the ideas of metaphysical science should be testable but some of them may win general acceptance without their being tested. Just as the theory of atoms existed only as a theoretical proposition for 2,500 years, until their existence was objectively established in the 20th century, when atoms ceased to be a theory and became the cornerstone of modern science, so the invisible energy or reality in the microworld, which seems to have a metaphysical origin and context and which supplies the universal control to everything, has yet to be proved, and scientists need to devise the techniques to investigate it, including new technology such as the Large

Hadron Collider being built in Geneva, which may be able to detect consequences of differing energy intensity. If, like atoms, this invisible energy can become the cornerstone of the new metaphysical science it will cease to be a metaphysical principle alone and will become a physical principle with a metaphysical origin and manifestation.

Metaphysical science can reverse the post-Renaissance reductionism of man. Man has been reduced from a medieval being with physical, psychological, spiritual and divine aspects to a Renaissance being with physical and psychological aspects alone (Humanism affirming body and mind but not soul, spirit or divine spark). Since the Renaissance, man has been further reduced and impoverished to physical aspects alone: atoms, cells and electrical discharges in the brain. Descartes reduced man's wholeness to a divided mind and body, Darwin reduced man's mind to an ape's, Freud reduced man's mind to a conscious part that was less important than his subconscious and unconscious parts. Copernicus has reduced man's anthropocentric standing at the centre of the universe to the standing of a marginal creature on a marginal star, and 20th century cosmology has reduced that standing still further, by demonstrating that man's star is just one of billions upon billions of stars in a thousand million galaxies.

Physicalist holism goes some way to restoring man's true standing, by seeing him as more than physical events and atoms, as an organism rising up through a hierarchy of wholes. Metaphysical Universalism reinstates his stature by seeing him as the only creature in the universe who is fully guided by the metaphysical Reality, and by reinstating a full anthropic principle: man's star is the only star where the conditions are right for a soul to contact the universal energy of the Fire or Light. Metaphysical science dignifies rather than demeans human values as the universe can once again be divinely inspired, be subject to human freewill and be anthropocentric (as man is able to receive the metaphysical Reality in his divine heart).

REDUCTIONISM, HOLISM AND UNIVERSALISM

It is now time to reverse the reductionism of metaphysics during the 18th, 19th and 20th centuries. Reductionism has reduced religion to the psychological activity of the soul and therefore to the level of psychological phenomena and eventually to physical processes. Likewise reductionism has reduced the metaphysical and mystical vision to psychological and physical processes. The onslaught on metaphysics in the past has been reductionist: to reduce the metaphysical Reality to reason (Kant), and then to reduce its propositions and concepts to meaninglessness (the Vienna Circle). The role of contemplation in metaphysics must be de-reductionised and reinstated, along with the rational justification for metaphysics and the intuitional vision of the Fire or Light.

It is no longer possible for philosophy and science to operate along reductionist lines, nor is it desirable for philosophers and scientists to take a gradual step forward in the direction of physicalist holism. For such gradualism will not fundamentally change anything. Change must be fundamental and qualitative rather than quantitative, and must be sudden, radical and abrupt to reinstate the metaphysical vision now, before another generation suffers from a fragmented or physicalist perspective.

*

Such a sudden and abrupt change involves a radical break with the past and constitutes a Metaphysical Revolution, which is a counter-revolution against dehumanising reductionism in philosophy and science, and against all the false theories which have held sway for too long in the 20th century and from which the younger generation need to be liberated.

In philosophy, the Revolution sweeps away much of the legacy of those who have practised reductionism for over 90 years: the whole movement of analytic and linguistic philosophy which was begun at the turn of the 20th century by Moore (1899) and Russell, who reacted against the absolute Idealism of Hegel; the logical atomism of Russell (1918-19) and the early Wittgenstein of the *Tractatus* (1922), the Logical Positivism of Carnap, Otto Neurath, Schlick, Tolman, Wittgenstein and Ayer (the Vienna Circle), and the linguistic analysis of later Wittgenstein (*Philosophical Investigations*, 1953) and Oxford philosophers such as the reductionist Ryle (*The Concept of Mind*, 1949) and Austin. In our time the tradition has been reasserted in Structuralism, deconstruction and Post-Structuralism, movements of the 1960s and 1970s and thereafter, which have confined reality to language and a text. Reality is not within language or a text alone, it can be known by the contemplating universal being, and Derrida is quite wrong to assert "il n'y a rien hors du texte".

Wittgenstein felt that the business of the philosopher is not to put forward any metaphysical theory, but to clear up conceptual confusions. I would say that the business of the philosopher is to clear up category confusions in the approach to Reality, the chief one being the distinction between reason and intuitional contemplation or higher intellect, and then to reinstate the concept of a metaphysical whole which manifests from outside Nature into Nature, and which enables us to interpret every element of our experience, including every possible concept. Philosophers must look outwards at the universe instead of logic-chopping over meanings. The subject of philosophy is again man in relation to the universe: in relation to visible Nature and the invisible forces known to physicists, poets and those working at the higher levels of Reality.

In philosophy the Revolution goes back to William James, Bergson, T.E. Hulme (in his Bergsonian phase), Whitehead and Husserl, c1910. This was soon after William James's *The Varieties of Religious Experience* appeared in 1902; and soon after Bergson's first meeting with Hulme in 1907, the year Bergson's process philosophy and "élan vital", which was to influence Whitehead, appeared in *Creative Evolution*. In 1910 Hulme and Whitehead may have been in the same room at the Aristotelian Society, Albemarle Street (of which Hulme was a member), under the chairmanship of G.E. Moore, when the discussion alternated between metaphysics and linguistic analysis; shortly before the appearance of Husserl's *Ideas* in 1913. At this time analytic and linguistic philosophy had not made gains, although between 1901 and 1910 Russell was collaborating with the early Whitehead and leading philosophy towards Logical Positivism. 1910 marked the beginning of the European civilisation's Breakdown of Certainties (stage 37 of the European civilisation's 61 stages in *The Fire and the Stones*). It is from this time that the threads must be picked up, and from our vantage point in 1992 we can see the vital impulse of vitalism and process metaphysics not as a T.H. Huxleyan determinism but as the metaphysical Fire or Light of Universalism. A new Metaphysics Society should be formed.

In science the Revolution sweeps away the legacy of those who have practised materialistic, mechanistic reductionism in physics, biology and other sciences, and also modifies the legacy of those who have settled for physicalist, non-granular, organic holism within the level of Existence, and have ignored the three higher levels of metaphysical Being. In science, the Revolution goes back to the 1920s holistic and organicist ideas, including Whitehead's *Process and Reality* (1929), and to the unfinished business of Newton, Einstein, Jung and Bohm. The crucial point in science was slightly later than in philosophy, c1917. Einstein could not reconcile his closed, static cosmological model of the universe of 1917 with his general relativity equations without adding an extra term to the equations - the cosmological constant (Newton's repulsive force which balances the attraction of gravity). Although his static model of the universe was overtaken by Hubble's discovery that the universe is expanding (1929), there is great interest in the cosmological constant today. After winning the Nobel Prize for Physics in 1921, Einstein sought the mathematical relationship between electromagnetism and gravitation, which would discover the laws governing everything in the universe, from electrons to planets, and which would relate the universal properties of matter and energy in a single equation or formula, a unified field theory. This search was undermined by the uncertainty principle of 1927, which Einstein never accepted, proposing hidden variables, condemning himself to isolation. His first version of a unified field theory was published in 1929, and a new version followed in 1950, which most physicists declared untenable. He handed on the baton to Bohm and died in 1955. The Revolution picks up the threads of Einstein's long and lonely search.

In all disciplines the Revolution spreads metaphysical science and demands a theory of absolutely everything, including the religious, spiritual, mystical and metaphysical Reality. In physics it asserts that the uncertainty principle of 1927 is incomplete and amounts to a "don't know", differences in electron and quark behaviour being due to relative intensity of the Fire or Light which acts as an expanding force or fifth force to counterbalance gravity, as a cosmological constant, a hidden variability, and as Bohm's principle of order which is filled with irreducible wisdom, understanding, love and thought (as mystics know) and unfolds consciousness from the quantum vacuum and, as the substance of Being, gives mass to all particles. In biology the Revolution asserts that the Fire or Light acts as an "élan vital", controls growth in terms of process and creates self-determining organisms, which are in fact determined by the controlling reality of the Fire or Light. In medicine it holds that the vital energy of the Fire or Light (the Hindu prana) passes into the body's energy system and the soul and charges them with life and vitality. In brain physiology is holds that mind is not dependent on body, but is associated with a Bose-Einstein condensate, photons which exist independently of the body and which use the body. In psychology, it goes back to Jung, who saw the mind as a self-regulating system (as in modern cybernetics) whose health is characterised by wholeness and unity, who recognised illumination (for example in his Introduction to

The Secret of the Golden Flower), and who had decidedly mystical leanings. In psychology the crucial date is again c1917, five years after Jung had published *Psychology of the Unconscious* (1912) and stopped collaborating with Freud, and a year after his lecture *La Structure de l'Inconscient* (1916), which developed the basis of the collective unconscious. In psychology the Revolution develops and metaphysicalises the insights of Jung and Sperry.

The reinstatement of metaphysics is a matter of urgency. Chairs of Metaphysics in philosophy and the sciences should reflect the new importance being accorded to metaphysics, metaphysical science and the Metaphysical Revolution.

In conclusion, reductionism, which still has its defenders, is a materialism and mechanism associated with classical physics, which has been overtaken by new organicist ideas associated with physicalist holism in biology and quantum physics. These ideas in turn have been overtaken by metaphysical ideas for a new metaphysical science and Universalism in all sciences and philosophy. Many hypotheses remain to be tested in both physicalist holism and metaphysical Universalism, and scientists and philosophers should now engage in this research.

Notes

1. Jan Smuts, *Holism and Evolution*. See also Ken Wilber, *Eye to Eye*, pp83-4.
2. Roger Sperry, *Structure and Significance of the Consciousness Revolution*.
3. See previous essay. (Universalism was introduced in *The Fire and the Stones*, 1991.)
4. See essay, *The Metaphysical Revolution*, in Nicholas Hagger's *Selected Poems: A Metaphysical's Way of Fire*, for a fuller account of metaphysics and what is hidden behind or within physics.
5. See J.J. Williamson, *The Structure of All*.
6. See René Guénon, *The Multiple States of Being*.

7. See *The Fire and the Stones: A Grand Unified Theory of World History and Religion*, Part One.
8. See pages 15-16, 24-25, 59-66.
9. Wilber, op cit, pp153, 180.
10. See Willis Harman, *Metaphysics, the Union Whose Time Has Come*.
11. See Willis Harman, *Global Mind Change*, p35.
12. See Willis Harman, *A Re-examination of the Metaphysical Foundations of Modern Science*.

APPENDIX 1

HISTORY, RELIGION AND TELEVISION

In 1991 an independent television production company, Diverse Production Ltd., wanted to make a television series about *The Fire and the Stones*. Peter Donebauer, the company's Executive Producer, and his producer Roy Ackerman had several discussions with Nicholas Hagger as to what form the treatment should take, and they considered a variety of approaches. Nicholas Hagger sketched out four alternative treatments or options. They are all of interest as they summarise his thinking on civilisations and religion, and complement some of the ideas in the previous three essays (for example setting Universalism in its historical context).

The first idea was to focus on how Nicholas Hagger came up with his Grand Unified Theory of civilisations, history and religion, and there was talk of visiting Japan to film. In the course of telling the story of the discovery there would be coverage of the Grand Unified Theory itself.

The second idea was to focus more on the history theory itself. Nicholas Hagger was asked to offer some thoughts on a possible series of three programmes on the Fire or Light as the central idea of civilisations.

The third idea emphasised the role of religions in the spread of civilisations and showed how specific religions are the dynamos of their civilisations.

The fourth idea involved seeing 10 religions in relation to their civilisations. Nicholas Hagger pared down 10 religions and their civilisations to a few lines which suggest what is happening now; a story; 3 or 4 filmable high points in the development of each civilisation; and theme.

The four alternative treatments are as follows:

1. A GRAND UNIFIED THEORY OF HISTORY
(This is of interest as it shows how Nicholas Hagger

arrived at his Grand Unified Theory of history.)

This programme presents a revolutionary theory of history, a new way of looking at history, not in terms of economics or individuals or politics but in terms of ideas and inspiration.

Light can be seen as particles or waves, and this theory sees history not as a collection of particle-like events but as waves (the rise and fall of civilisations) with pattern. It presents the first ever Grand Unified Theory of world history.

How did I come up with a theory which presents a grand unified view of world history?

1. When lecturing in Iraq and Japan in the 1960s I attempted to relate the individual and his experience to a historical process. (Compare similar efforts by other writers.)

2. My particular experience enabled me to step outside the culture I grew up in and search among other cultures. While teaching Gibbon, Spengler and Toynbee in Japan I saw a fourth way of understanding history: a common historical process in different cultures.

3. When in Japan I visited a Zen temple and saw that the vision of the Fire or Light is transmitted in Japan but not in the modern European civilisation. I was reminded of the 17th century Metaphysical poets I had read, who are full of the Fire or Light which can barely be found in Literature after c1880.

4. During my time in Iraq, Japan and Libya I travelled throughout the Middle and Far East, and visited China, Russia, South-East Asia, India and Egypt. I analysed the development of several different civilisations from the remains of civilisations that have died, and found that the "stones" (ruins of temples, cathedrals and mosques) were inspired by the Fire.

5. Seeking to see how civilisations started, I looked for a common process and found it in a migration which led to the flowering of a new religion round the vision of the Fire.

6. I thought that if civilisations grow round a strong religion, it is logical to suppose that they decay when the religion decays. I found there was a correlation.

7. I then researched the detail of the stages, analysing each culture to see if it fitted. In the course of repeated analysis a pattern emerged.

8. The pattern shows the stage living civilisations have reached in the course of their development, and, being a Grand Unified Theory, has predictive implications. The Byzantine-Russian civilisation is older than the European civilisation, which is older that the North American civilisation.

The theory challenges the sceptical line of thinking and is happy to do so.

2. THE RISE AND FALL OF CIVILISATIONS (UNDERSTANDING OUR TIME: A "STAGES" VIEW OF HISTORY)

(This scenario presents Nicholas Hagger's theory of history with great conciseness. The whole idea is here in embryo, and it is printed with page references to key passages in *The Fire and the Stones* so that a student can go to the original and familiarise himself with the details of the theory.)

A series of three television programmes suggesting a Grand Unified Theory that explains both the rise and decay of all previous civilisations. By comparing our own civilisation with previous ones we can predict what is ahead for us in the coming centuries.

(1) The Rise of Civilisations: the Central Idea of the Fire and its God

We all want to understand the history of our own time. The end of the Cold War, the collapse of the Soviet empire in Eastern Europe, America's world dominance, moves towards a United States of Europe are all bewildering to us in the 1990s. What is happening? Are there different civilisations that rise and fall? If so, why do civilisations rise and fall? We see a Persian carpet with a pattern. Is there a pattern in history and can it help us to anticipate the future?

Like light in physics, which is both particles and waves, history can be seen as concrete particle-like events, as a random flux with no civilisations; and as waves which suggest patterns. Past attempts to find pattern revolve round civilisations but see them as victims of moral decadence, religion and barbarians (Gibbon), growing old (Spengler), responding to challenges (Toynbee), and being subject to a law of civilisation and decay that contrasts with barbarism (Adams).

My new attempt sees pattern in terms of civilisations which have a central idea and go through 61 stages in a rainbow-like parabola. The central idea is not the conquests of conquerors like Alexander the Great, Napoleon, Hitler and their generals, or economics (capitalism or Marxism), but the central vision and experience of all religions, the Fire or Light. Civilisations grow when someone (a mystic, e.g. Mohammed) has an experience of the divine Fire (which in Mohammed's case became the *Koran*) and this passes into the religion, round which a civilisation grows. Civilisations decay when the vision weakens, and the civilisation turns secular.

I have produced a Grand Unified Theory of world history and religion which explains the rise and fall of all living and dead civilisations. Unlike Toynbee's work of 12 volumes, *The Fire and the Stones* is compressed into one volume by using tabulation. I call my 900 pages a "prolegomena" to a massively long work which may or may not eventually be written. I present a "stages" view of civilisations which offers a clear way of understanding the history of our own time.

What is the Fire which is the central idea of civilisations? In the European civilisation it is the vision of the Light of the World, Jesus Christ, which was renewed by Cassian, St. Benedict, Gregory the Great, St. Hildegard, St. Bernard and the European mystics to T.S. Eliot (pp873-4), and which was originally embodied in the King. We see the King as a Sacred Ruler who embodies the Fire (pp659-661). In the Indian civilisation the Fire is to be found in the enlightenment of the Buddha and Mahavira; it is samadhi. It is Japanese satori and Islamic Sufi fana. It is identified with gods and has many religious expressions (p874). It inspired the "stones", the cathedrals, temples and mosques (pp875-6).

This Fire has been known since c20,000BC and before. It originated in Central Asia and passed among the Indo-Europeans, and is then found in the Kuro-Araxes culture, Sumeria, the Danube region, Egypt and South America, where long barrows and ziggurats/pyramids can be found. We look at Sumeria and Egypt (where the "akh" is the illuminated soul). The diffusionist view in history sees trade as passing from culture to culture, as does McNeill's *The Rise of the West*, which discounts civilisations. In the same way the Fire moved from region to region, from Central Asia to the Indo-European area, Sumeria, Egypt, Greece, Anatolia, Syria, among the Hebrews and the Celts, to Iran, India, China and eventually to the Essenes. We can link civilisations and show how the vision of the Fire has been transmitted in a perpetual flow.

The philosophy of history traditionally falls into two camps, one speculative, one analytical. The speculative view assumes history is linear or cyclical, and not a random flux without pattern (St. Augustine, Bossuet, Toynbee, Gibbon). The analytical view is sceptical and based on empirical observation (pp350-2). This view denies pattern on seven grounds (pp353-4) which we refute. We see history as one global field (with Toynbee) rather than as many national fields, but we also see it (unlike McNeill) as civilisations, not cultures.

We distinguish between "culture" and "civilisation" (pp357-9). Cultures develop into civilisations. Using our 6-

point criteria for what a "civilisation" is once it has developed beyond a "culture", we identify 25 civilisations and discuss our identification (pp360-8). The fundamental point is that a civilisation has its own distinctive religion with its own distinctive god (pp366-7).

Evidence for our view of civilisations as being Fire-based comes from the tradition of the Fire (eye-witness accounts) and from the findings of our comparative study of the growth of civilisations. (Most theories of civilisations are about their decay, there is not much about their growth. Toynbee never found what caused the differentiation of civilisations at their genesis, i.e. the Fire, and had to resort to "challenge and response".)

We see how civilisations grow round the Fire, their metaphysical central idea. We highlight the European civilisation while referring to the other 24 civilisations. The Fire of a new civilisation starts in an earlier civilisation (in the case of the European civilisation, the Fire or Light of Christ, the Light of the World, which originated in the Israelite civilisation). The mystic experience of the Fire is brought to the new civilisation as a result of a migration (in the case of Europe, the Palestinian migration to Britain and Rome). This conquers and absorbs the new culture (in Europe, that of the Teutonic barbarians in Britain and of the Romans in Italy).

The Fire becomes established in a collective movement which we call a religion. The Fire creates a new religion (in Europe through British Christianity and Roman Catholicism) before the genesis of the new civilisation (which took place in the 5th century AD in Europe).

The Fire of the new religion creates the growing civilisation's central idea. There have been 16 alternative views of a civilisation's central idea (pp394-5) and these are refuted (pp395-403). The Fire is the most suitable central idea as it attracts heterogeneous peoples and cultures, and unifies and sustains a growing civilisation.

The Fire is strong during growth and has an impact on the peoples' cultures and leaves physical evidence for the strength of its civilisation in buildings and artefacts. We call these "the stones",which the Fire has inspired (pp875-6). The peoples are attracted to the new civilisation's religion (in the European civilisation's case, Christianity, as expressed in the churches at Glastonbury and Rome).

There is a doctrinal controversy (in Europe, as to whether or not Christ should be shown with an image) and there is a shift from the existing god to a rising god who assumes new importance and brings about a religious unification. This leads to political unification (in Europe, Charlemagne). Later there is a schism which weakens and ends the civilisation's growth (in Europe, the split of 867 and later 1054).

We see that a foreign threat deals a military blow which arrests the civilisation's growth (in Europe, the invasions of c900 by Vikings, Spanish Moslems and Magyars). The blow arrests the civilisation's growth for 50 years and secularizes it as the State widens its powers and controls the religion, including the Fire, which is therefore in decline.

In due course the growing civilisation has a counterthrust and achieves a territorial expansion which lasts 200-500 years and it recovers its growth round a new interpretation of the central idea of the Fire (c951-1244 in Europe, round the cult of Mary). The god of Fire-made growth appears in heroic epic (in Europe, the Grail romances). Illustrations from other civilisations.

All civilisations rise and grow through this same pattern. In due course we can link civilisations (see chart 1 in *The Fire and the Stones*) and show how this vision of the Fire has been transmitted and how it connects all civilisations. We can thus see that this vision gives a unity of religious inspiration, not a conflict.

The next programme will resume the story at the beginning of the breakdown of civilisations. We will see that the human response to the Fire which is the driving force of new civilisations is the force of renewal within established civilisations and that the mystic is central to history rather than a marginal oddity or madman.

(2) The Breakdown and Renewal of Civilisations: the New People and their Heretical God

In the last programme we saw that the central idea of religions and civilisations is the Fire; and we traced the story of the rise of civilisations through their first 16 stages. Now we resume the story.

Our theme is the breakdown and renewal of civilisations, in which there is a transfer of power from the people who have ruled the civilisation to a new people, who follow a heresy. The turning point is a military blow which destroys the confidence of the old rulers and secularizes their religion. In telling this story we continue to highlight the European civilisation and draw parallels from the other 24 civilisations. We see how the growing civilisation's metaphysical central idea is weakened (i.e. secularized), then strengthened, then weakened again.

We have seen that the renewal of growth through a change of emphasis in the growing civilisation's religion is now the orthodoxy, and in each civilisation a rising people throws up a new Fire-based sect which is deemed heretical (in the European civilisation, the personal Church-free God of the Templars, Cathars, Lollards and Hussites). This sect is persecuted (e.g. the Albigensian Crusade). Partly as a result of the heretical sect and partly on account of foreign influence, the organised religion declines (c1244-1453 in Europe). Mystics try to reverse this decline (in Europe the 14th century mystics).

We show how a military blow heralds the civilisation's breakdown (in the case of Europe in 1453, the Ottoman conquest of the Christian Byzantine civilisation). Breakdown lasts about 100 years (in Europe, 1453-1553). The civilisation is paralysed, defence becomes paramount, and the State escapes the control of religion and becomes defensive, secularizing the Fire (in Europe, the Reformation states being independent of Rome). The growing civilisation has lost its confidence as a result of the military blow, and it turns away from its own culture and revives the past culture of another civilisation (in Europe, the Renaissance). The heresy of a rising people now meets further resistance from the established rulers in whose hands the civilisation has broken down, and this resistance leads to civil war (in Europe, in 1546-1555, the German Protestant princes against the Spanish Catholics).

We show that there is now a shift of emphasis in the civilisation's religion; and a new people or dynasty (in Europe, the Renaissance Humanists) take over the heresy and graft it onto the central idea (in Europe, creating the Protestant God and Christ). This weakens the non-heretical central idea and at the same time brings freshness associated with change. We see that the new people renew the civilisation's central idea in the short term while weakening it in the long term.

Other examples of new people and their heresy (pp503-506). We contrast the gods of the central idea in all 25 civilisations with the new heretical gods (illustrations between pp430 and 431 which are taken from pp411-5 and 507-9).

We show that the new people now expand geographically (in Europe, 1555-1778, voyages of discovery and European colonisation) to reverse the shock of the military blow. There are now seceders from the new people; they create a stronger Fire than the new people's (in Europe, Puritanism), which can affect another civilisation (in the case of Europe, North America). The new people persecute them (in Europe, anti-Puritan and anti-Huguenot activities) and the new people's religion prevails. There is a bout of scientific materialism inspired by another civilisation (in Europe, the Industrial Revolution inspired by Arab science in Spain and by the Renaissance's import of Arab books from the libraries of Constantinople after 1453), and an artistic reaction to it (Romanticism). We show that the heirs of the new people undergo a further expansion into empire, which is a substitution for growth and overextends and further secularizes the civilisation, and groups attempt to renew the Fire (in Europe, as a result of Romanticism). The civilisation's energy is dispersed abroad and it goes into decline, and the Fire disappears from the official religion (in Europe, c1880). As a result, a generation later there is a breakdown of certainties (in Europe, c1910-1914), the central idea weakens, the visual arts become restless (in Europe, Modernism, c1870-1930), and scepticism develops in philosophy (in Europe, Logical Positivism and Linguistic Analysis). We note that scepticism is an aspect of the flow of history and surfaces at a distinct point.

The civilisation is overextended and goes into imperial decline (in Europe, c1914-1997). In the course of this there is colonial conflict (in Europe, two civil wars and decolonising challenges from the North American and Byzantine-Russian civilisations), and as a result the civilisation concedes decolonisation (in Europe, the postwar collapse of the European empires) and there is increasing proletarianisation and egalitarianism at home.

We show that there is a surrender of sovereignty - at the urging of the winner of the colonial conflict (in Europe's case North America) - to a politically unified conglomerate (in Europe, a coming United States of Europe) which acts as a secularizing foreign influence (in Europe's case from Brussels). We distinguish between union and federalism. Illustrations of other such unified conglomerates, including Cyrus's Achaemenian Persian Empire, Communism in the Byzantine-Russian and Chinese civilisations, and the British Raj in India.

We now see what stage the U.S. is in. We establish that the U.S. is a separate civilisation and not a colony (unlike the new Israel, which is effectively a colonial outpost rather than a new civilisation). The North American civilisation is much younger that the European civilisation and has reached stage 15 of its 61 stages as opposed to Europe's stage 43 (the coming conglomerate). The U.S. is a quarter through, Europe two thirds. The North American civilisation began with a migration from Europe (c1494-

APPENDIX

1650). This brought a Protestant-Puritan Christ and Fire which drew together the North American and Canadian peoples and inspired American "stones" (cathedrals and churches). There was doctrinal controversy (the Puritan Christ versus the revivalist Christ of the Great Awakening, 1725-1750) and this led to religious unification and then to political unification (the federal constitution of the 13 original colonies which became states).

Growth followed this with the creation of the United States. There was schism (the Christ of the Reformation churches brought by the immigrants versus the new evangelical Protestant Christ, c1860) and a foreign threat which delivered a military blow (the secessionist Confederacy sought foreign aid as an independent, hostile power). The growth of the new civilisation was arrested (c1861-1913), and we show that then there was a counterthrust (c1913 to present) which won the two world wars and left the U.S., like Rome after the two Punic Wars, poised for an increased world role as the only superpower.

We conclude that North America is still growing with a metaphysical Fire in its religion, Christianity, and a heresy forming, Universalism which will emerge from the New Age; whereas Europe is decaying with a secularized, sceptical vision. Compare Rome and Byzantium after 330AD. (Gibbon wrongly saw the Byzantine civilisation as a continuation of the Roman civilisation and not as a separate civilisation with an Orthodox religion that continued with its Russian Orthodox phase as a Byzantine-Russian civilisation).

Western civilisation is the European civilisation plus the North American civilisation. Our stages view disagrees with the view of Spengler (that the West is growing old) and Toynbee (who does not separate the European and North American civilisations, who sees the Byzantines as continuing into the Ottoman period despite the change in religion, and who sees uniform chunks of 400 year periods, rather than stages with varying time lengths). We also

131

disagree with McNeill (who does not see stages/patterns, only concrete events). We also disagree with Paul Kennedy (who, lacking the stages view, sees the American civilisation as being in decline), and with Fukuyama (who sees the end of the Cold War as Hegel's end of history rather than as the end of stage 41 of Europe's 61 stages, a stage that helped the expansion of North America's expansive stage 15).

The next programme will carry our story forward to see where the other living civilisations stand (the Byzantine-Russian, Arab, Indian, Chinese, Japanese, South American and African civilisations).

(3) The Fall of Civilisations: Federalism and Foreign Occupation

In the last programme we took the development of civilisations to stage 43 and we saw that the European civilisation is about to reach stage 43 of its 61 stages, a politically unified conglomerate (the coming United States of Europe). So far civilisations have been in charge of their own destiny, though in the course of the colonial conflict part of the civilisation can be occupied (in Europe, France by Germany, Eastern Europe by the Soviet Union). Now increasingly the story is one of dwindling independence and sovereignty and foreign occupation. Many of our living civilisations have not reached their closing stages; we can anticipate what these will be by comparing their coming stages with those of dead civilisations which have, on reaching stage 61, passed into other living civilisations.

Stage 43 is a politically unified conglomerate under the influence of the civilisation which won its colonial conflict (in Europe's case, the North American civilisation). So far we have highlighted the European civilisation and supplemented this with images from the other 24 civilisations. We cannot continue to do this because Europe has not reached stage 46, and so we will highlight the other main living civilisations: the Byzantine-Russian civilisation (which reached stage 43 under American- and European-backed Bolsheviks c1918-1991); the Arab civilisation (in stage 43 under the European civilisation c1881-1980); the Chinese civilisation (in stage 43 under Russian-backed Communists from 1948); the Japanese civilisation (in stage 43 under the North American civilisation from 1945); the South American civilisation, i.e. Andean and Meso-American civilisations (in stage 43 under the European civilisation c1572-1810); and the African civilisation (in stage 43 under the European civilisation c1914-1980).

We see that the civilisation's Fire is weak now, and that under the influence of the cosmopolitan conglomerate there is syncretism and Universalism (stage 44) in which the Fire is seen as the common source of all religions. Universalism has surfaced in previous cosmopolitan stages (15, 29 and 34), and a civilisation in stage 15 influences another civilisation in stage 44. The North American civilisation is in stage 15, and the first sign of its Universalist heretical vision is in the preaching (proclaiming the salvation of all souls) of George de Benneville and of the semi-Calvinist John Murray who migrated from Europe to colonial America in 1741 and 1770 respectively, and of the Unitarian Hosea Ballou, who denied the divinity of Christ at the end of the 18th century. 20th century Universalism explores the universal element of all religions, and in 1961 the Universalist Church of America and the American Unitarian Association amalgamated as the Unitarian Universalist Association. Universalism has come to be associated with the New Ages's interest in the universal element of all religions, and can be expected to be associated with Europe's Universalist stage 44. Illustrations of Byzantine-Russian, Chinese, Japanese and Arab syncretism.

Later there is discontent with foreign rule and there is a revival of the civilisation's cultural purity (stage 45), as has happened with the emergence of Yeltsin's Russia and the return of the Russian Orthodox Fire and rites, and as is beginning to happen in Japan following Akihito's accession. In this stage Europe can expect a new Baroque movement, as stage 45 is rooted in stage 28. (We note the contrast between the Western European stage 43-44 attitude towards the EC and the Eastern European nationalistic stage 45 secessions from their Communist conglomerate.) We show that there is now a further attempt at a counterthrust under a foreign Federalist influence to restore past glories and greatness. Federalism means that different nationalities recover their sovereignty and independence in internal affairs but are linked externally. In Russia this is happening now: as the CIS becomes a Federation of post-Communist republics. This move was predicted in *The Fire and the Stones*, which is known in some quarters as the book which foretold the end of Communism. In the Arab civilisation, the search for a Federation of Arab states, which Gaddafi has always wanted. In the future, both China and Japan will split into their component parts, which will be internally independent. Compare the Latin American OAS and African OAU.

At the end of the Federalist period the decline intensifies. There is mega-inflation and economic decline (as in some South American states), and the Fire ceases to be publicly recognised by the civilisation's religion. Foreign invaders undermine the civilisation's religion. We now highlight the ancient Egyptian civilisation (perhaps the Roman and Greek civilisations as well). Egypt was occupied by the Seleucids c332-168. The invaders destroy some of the stones, the monuments inspired by the Fire of the growing civilisation's religion. The civilisation's central idea becomes forgotten. In Egypt Re gave way to the Seleucids' Zeus. There is a final independent phase or swansong (in Egypt c168-30BC). A foreign power again occupies the civilisation (in Egypt, the Romans c30BC-395AD, beginning with the events surrounding Antony and Cleopatra). There is further secularization of the civilisation's Fire under the foreign power's religion, and the civilisation's mystics turn from their own religion to that of foreign cults (in Egypt, from Re to Jupiter and Byzantine

Christianity). The civilisation resists the foreign occupier at different times, but the mystics defect (in Egypt from Roman Jupiter to Gnosticism, Christianity and Neo-platonism). They are persecuted, and coteries are formed, which continue the central idea (in Egypt, in the Isis Mysteries).

We now consider the decay and demise of civilisations. There is a further occupation (in Egypt, under the Byzantines c395-616). The Fire-less religion of the original civilisation is suppressed and dies (in Egypt, Re under Byzantine Christianity). There is a sudden final conquest of the religionless civilisation (in Egypt, under the Persians and Arabs, 628, 639). The civilisation finally passes into another civilisation (the Egyptian civilisation into the Arab civilisation). How all the dead civilisations have passed into the Celtic, Arab, Byzantine-Russian or European civilisations.

We have revealed a Universalist pattern of linear-cyclical spirals (pp354-5) which unites linear and cyclical views of history by seeing a spiralling rainbow. Stages are similar in all civilisations and relate to the whole like fractals. The Universalist pattern (pp643-5). The varying time-scale between civilisations (pp654-5). The geographical and other reasons why some civilisations have lasted around 4,000 years whereas others have lasted only 1,500 years. (We disagree with Toynbee who sees a broadly uniform time-pattern in all civilisations.) The role of contemplative mystics in creating and renewing civilisations; they are central to their civilisations, not marginal oddities.

Predictions of coming Federalisms and foreign occupations. Comparing living civilisations with dead civilisations, we can make some fairly specific predictions (based on pp 685-696). America will found a world Empire in the 21st and 22nd centuries and absorb the Federations of South America, India and Africa. Europe will be politically integrated for 150 years. Russia will be linked with Europe. The Arabs will form a pan-Arab Federation and will be occupied by Europe following a westward invasion of

Europe (probably from the Moslem states of the southern Russian republics). Japan will form a Far-Eastern or Pacific Community (an Eastern civilisation) and will eventually be occupied by America. We see that civilisations are always occupied by other civilisations at an earlier stage than themselves.

The North American civilisation will enter a world-wide stage in the 21st and 22nd centuries (pp 703ff), and an American-led world-wide Universalist religion is ahead (pp 715ff), contrary to the views of Fukuyama and Paul Kennedy. America's world-wide culture and cultural Empire will be like the Romans'. Images of the similarity between the U.S. and Rome.

We conclude that a world-wide culture is possible, with a basis, like all other cultures, in the Fire. The American heresy which will become the new orthodoxy in the North American civilisation is an embryonic Universalism that has grown out of the New Age; it is already affecting stage 44 of the European civilisation.

We end in the present and with the need to renew the Fire which (as its central idea) renews our civilisation and delays the time when it will be conquered by another civilisation. Christianity has largely forgotten the Fire. There needs to be a movement to re-emphasise the Fire, a goal of the Metaphysical Revolution which is already taking place (pp 718ff) and which combats scepticism (itself a symptom of stage 39 of the European civilisation) and challenges the Vienna Circle's sceptical view of the universe which has dominated Western thought. The Metaphysical Revolution is supported by thinking in subatomic physics throughout the century (e.g. Einstein, Bohm and others).

We leave the viewer with the understanding that all his ways of looking are themselves products of a "stages" view of history, that scepticism is a product of stage 39 rather than of the coming stages 44 and 45. How my view has led to an entirely new way of understanding history as patterned waves rather than as particle-like events. It is a view that enables us to understand our time.

136

APPENDIX

FOOTNOTE: Historical Developments since early 1991

Since I published *The Fire and the Stones* in April 1991 the U.S.S.R. and its stage 43 empire has come to an end and so has Communism. President Yeltsin has banned the Communist Party. (I predicted these developments in the book, and associated them with Yeltsin on page 675.) The USSR has been replaced by the CIS which is still groping towards the federalism of stage 46 and is hard up. The position of the southern Moslem states in the former USSR has become more volatile as local wars and Moslem loyalties re-emerge.

Central Europe has been constantly in the news. Yugoslavia has broken up following the death of the Yugoslavian Communist Party in 1990, and Croatia, Slovenia and Bosnia-Hercegovina have all fought for their freedom from central Serbian control. These states are gathering to be admitted into a United States of Europe, along with Hungary, Poland and Czechoslovakia, which is set to break into separate regions for Czechs and Slovaks.

The Maastricht Treaty of December 1991 aimed at creating "an ever closer union among the peoples of Europe". Title 1, Article A of the Treaty states: "By this Treaty the High Contracting Parties establish among themselves a European Union." Article 8 continues: "Every person holding the nationality of a Member State shall be a citizen of the Union. Citizens of the Union shall enjoy the rights conferred by this Treaty and shall be subject to the duties imposed thereby." All Europeans thus become citizens of a new state, which is a union. (In *The Fire and the Stones*, I show stage 43 as a "union", which is ahead for Europe.) The Maastricht Treaty vested competence over almost every area of modern government in the institutions of Europe, which have absolute discretion in delegating or not delegating downwards and merely pay lip service to "subsidiarity" (the doctrine that less should be done by the EC institutions and more by national governments or bodies close to the people) in areas such as the environment and animal welfare.

In practical terms, Brussels has the initiative in all member states and the EC permeates life in all government departments, dominating the thinking of Ministers in the Foreign Office, Home Office, Employment, Social Security, Transport, Trade and Industry and (currently) Environment. The EC dominates the Treasury's monetary and fiscal policies in each state.

The future of Europe seems less certain after the Danish rejection of the 1991 Maastricht Treaty in a referendum in June 1992. In fact the underlying movement towards a United States of Europe is irreversible in the long term and no amount of rallying can undo it (not even the UK's temporary withdrawal from the ERM in September 1992), even though in the short term it seems as if it can be undone. All it needs is one nuclear incident, in which a former USSR nuclear weapon finds its way into Moslem hands, and the external threat will accelerate the collective defence of Europe under one umbrella, and therefore the process of union. By 2010 there could be a 42-nation Europe stretching from the Atlantic to the Urals, composed of 700 million people: the UK, Ireland, Denmark, the Netherlands, Belgium, Luxembourg, Germany, France, Portugal, Spain, Italy and Greece (already members); Norway, Sweden, Finland, Switzerland and Austria (to be admitted 1995-6?); Iceland, Malta, Cyprus (to be admitted 1996-99?); Poland, Czechoslovakia and Hungary (to be admitted 1999?); Estonia, Latvia, Lithuania, Romania, Bulgaria, Slovenia, Croatia, Bosnia, Serbia, Montenegro, Macedonia, Albania and Turkey (to be admitted 2000-05?); and Belarus, Ukraine, Moldova, Georgia, Armenia and Azerbaijan (to be admitted 2005-10?).

The Europe of 42 could well be more if some of the above countries fragment, for example Belgium into Flemings and Walloons, Czechoslovakia into Czech lands and Slovakia, and the U.K. into Britain and Scotland (or even England, Wales and Scotland). Europe will soon be approaching the 50 states (including Alaska and Hawaii) which form the

APPENDIX

United States of America.

The Gulf War has confirmed the U.S. as the only superpower. Its precision bombing and space probes demonstrate awesomely accurate technology, and it has a Roman power that enables it to take a foreign leader like Noriega prisoner, return him to the U.S. and sentence him to 40 years' imprisonment for cocaine-trafficking (compare the Roman capture of the British Caractacus). It increasingly seems possible that eventually America will get fed up with local wars and will impose a world order or empire (perhaps through the U.N.) to keep the peace. Starving countries as hard up as Russia will be glad of American dollars and protection if peace can be guaranteed. The world order will link all countries to one television network with a universal language, and will permit one region to select the television station of any other region at the push of a button.

3. RELIGION AND CIVILISATION

(The following notes for six programmes are of interest as they show how all the major religions share key themes, one of the tenets of Universalism. Page numbers refer to key passages in *The Fire and the Stones*.)

(1) The Rise and Fall of the Fire

General introduction and then focus on the Egyptian civilisation as an example of a dead civilisation.

1. Examples of the Fire
   In the European civilisation the best two examples are St Augustine and Hildegard. (See pp4-5. Also see 873-4, and the list of those who have known the Fire on p348 para 3.) The Fire today in poetry. Eliot, "The fire and the rose are one." Yeats, "O sages standing in God's holy fire." Also in my poems.

2. How the Fire Rises and Falls

This is an abstract of the "key themes" heading for programmes 1-6 below. A contemplative mystic has a vision of the Fire which migrates to a new area and forms a new religion. This becomes associated with the State, and increases the power of a priestly class who performs its rites. Peoples are attracted to the Fire and a political unification takes place around it. The Fire inspires the civilisation's expansion. Foreign invaders create a revival of a past culture, the religion turns worldly and undergoes a Reformation, and a new people adopt a heresy as the new orthodoxy. There is another expansion. Eventually the religion declines. This decline is associated with decolonisation. The Fire is now absent, the civilisation enters a conglomerate and is increasingly secularized. Eventually after a period of federalism, the civilisation is occupied and it ends up passing under its successor's religion.

Compare my view with Gibbon, Spengler and Toynbee.

3. What Happened in the Egyptian Religion and Civilisation (There can be side references to Mesopotamian ziggurats and to the Fire ceremony associated with Tammuz.)

(a) Experience of the Fire

Divine Sun-god by 2750BC, akh (Shining one). Egyptian *Book of the Dead*, Pyramid (pyr = fire). Texts to quote, see pp 29-33. (Christine, the Egyptian Temple-Dancer who danced at the launch of *The Fire and the Stones*, can dance the descent of the Fire of Amun.)

(b) Growth of Egyptian Religion

The Fire was brought from the Indo-European Kurgan and Mesopotamian civilisations to Memphis c3400BC and absorbed the Lower Kingdom by c3000 under a religion of Re which attracted the Egyptian peoples, assimilated Horus (in the north) after the union of Upper and Lower Egypt and inspired Pyramids, temples and obelisks under a divine king. After that, Re was slowly replaced by the heretical sect of Amun which became a new orthodoxy, and which was briefly challenged by Aton. The religion of Re, Amun, Horus-Osiris-Isis declined under foreign occupation and was eventually suppressed under the Byzantines, and Egyptian religion eventually passed into Islam, surviving underground in mystery cults (e.g. Isis Mysteries).

(c) Consequent Growth and Development of the Egyptian Civilisation

Unification of Old Kingdom c2686BC under a divine king, long stability until the military blow of the first Hyksos, then the expansion into the Middle Kingdom Empire (2110-1786). The heretical sect of Amun appeared. Egyptian religion declined under pressure from the Hyksos who delivered a military blow in c1674BC. In the subsequent 100 years' confusion the divine king became human. Under the Hyksos there was a revival of interest in Canaanite culture, and a civil war which created a new people, the New Kingdom Thebans who worshipped Amun, the heresy becoming an orthodoxy. The Fire of Amun, expansion into the New Kingdom empire in Southern Egypt and Asia. The rise and defeat of Aton, the god of Akhenaton. Restoration of Amun under Tutankhamun. Further expansion of the empire under the Tanites and Libyans (1085-730). Colonial conflict involving the Kushites (730) was finally won by the Assyrians (664) who controlled the Saite conglomerate. Universalism as Egyptian and Greek gods drew together, and revival of the Old Kingdom outlook. Federalism under the Achaemenian Persian Empire, invasion by Alexander and Seleucids. Independence from the Seleucids and Romans, mystics turned to Roman cults and Christianity and were persecuted. Occupation by the Byzantines, obliterating the old religion of the Egyptian Royal Mysteries.

4. Key Themes
   1. The Fire as the central idea of Egyptian religion in relation to Indo-European origins.
   2. Spread of the religion of Re among Egyptian peoples.

3. Creation of State rites around the Great Pyramid.
4. Priesthood's control of Egyptian society.
5. Old Kingdom linked to the Fire.
6. Re religion carried Egyptian expansion in Middle Kingdom against the Hyksos.
7. The Hyksos' conquest of Egypt in 1674 created a Canaanite Renaissance.
8. Worldly religion created an Amun Reformation under Thebans and more puritanical Atonites.
9. Heretical New Kingdom Thebans created an expansionist empire in Southern Egypt and Asia.
10. Decline of the religion of Amun associated with decolonisation before the Saite period.
11. Saite Assyrian foreign influence, and federalism under Persians.
12. Weak secularized religion and occupation by Seleucids, Romans, Byzantines and finally Arabs.

5. End

From the Egyptian civilisation we have seen how the Fire rose and fell, how the Fire was central to the religion of Re and how this had consequences in creating an expanding civilisation; and how the absence of the Fire led to a decline and foreign conquest.

There was a spread of Fire which passed from civilisation to civilisation (see Chart 1) and which will end up in the American world-wide civilisation.

(2) Islam
(Iran was its own civilisation until 1511, when it died into the Arab civilisation. Turkey was Byzantine until 1453 and Ottoman until 1920.)

1. What Happened in Islam and the Arab Civilisation
(a) Experience of the Fire

Mohammed's Fire c605, Sufi fana, ecstasy of Bayazid and Al-Hallaj, intoxicating Light expressed in terms of tavern, quote Omar Khayyam. Suhrawardi.

APPENDIX

(b) Growth of Islamic Religion

The Fire was brought from the Israelite civilisation to Arabia after c721BC (end of Israel), and created a new religion of Dhu (Lord) c325AD, and Allah (by 622), who attracted the Arabian peoples via Mohammed and inspired mosques. Split between Sunni and Shi'ites (from 661). Heretical sect of Theosophical Sufism (Suhrawardi). This heresy became an orthodoxy under a new people, the Ottomans. Decline of Islam before Europeans. Revival of Islamic Fundamentalism.

(c) Consequent Growth and Development of the Arab Civilisation

Unification of Mohammed's ummah or Moslem community (622), split of Sunnis and Shi'ites. Military blow from Byzantines (740). Abbasid Caliphate's expansion 790-1055. Decline of Islamic religion before Seljuq Turks and Mongols, who took Baghdad (1258). Il Khanate of Persia's revival, civil war between Mongols and Mamluk Sultanate (and Byzantines) against the Ottomans, the new people whose heresy, the Fire of Theosophical Sufism/Sunnism, became the new orthodoxy. Expansion of the Ottoman Empire (including Balkans) 1358-1683. The rise and defeat of Sufi Shi'ites. Iran passed into the Arab Empire after its conquest by Islamic Safavids (1501-11). Further expansion of the Ottoman Empire and Iranian Moslem Europe (1683-1798), until the colonial conflict which involved Europeans, e.g. in Egypt (1798). Religion weakened before Europeans, decline of the Ottoman Empire and decolonisation before Europeans. Loss of sovereignty to a European colonial conglomerate under the foreign influence of European Empires, c1881-1980. Birth of Turkey. Moslem revival of Fundamentalist Islamic values (1956-1980, Nasser, Gaddafi, Khomenei) during renewed independence and moves to Federalism (e.g. attempts at Arab Federation by Nasser and Gaddafi).

2. Key Themes

1. The Fire as the central idea of Islam in relation to

Israelite origins.
2. Spread of Islam among Arabian and Arab tribes drawn by Fire.
3. Secularization of Islam into an Arab Empire and State rites at Mecca.
4. Caliphs' increasing political power.
5. Birth and growth of Mohammed's ummah and Caliphate.
6. Allah religion carried Abbasid expansion 790-1055.
7. Mongol conquest of Baghdad created a Renaissance (revival of Il Khanate of Persia).
8. Worldly Caliph created Ottomans' Sufi-Sunni Reformation.
9. Heretical Theosophical Ottomans created expansion of the Ottoman Empire into the Balkans and elsewhere.
10. Decline of Islamic religion was associated with decolonisation before the Europeans.
11. European imperialist foreign influence, leading to new federalism.

3. Today and Significance of the Past in relation to the Future

Revival of Fundamentalist Islam under Nasser, Gaddafi, Khomenei. Events in Iran, Libya, Egypt (the assassination of Saddat) and Algeria. Mention of Pakistan. Turkey's links of language and culture with southern ex-Soviet states. Iran's possible purchase of 3 nuclear bombs for £82 million from the ex-USSR, probably Kazakhstan (according to the Paris-based *Al-Watan al-Arabi*), although this is denied by Iran. Pakistan's nuclear bomb. Attempts by Gaddafi and Saddam to obtain nuclear weapons. A potentially hostile federal Islam. Europe and Russia drawing together, under the influence of the U.S.A., to shield Western civilisation against Islam's nuclear threat.

Coming Federation of Arab and Islamic states through Arab League (including southern ex-Soviet states) adopting Federalism (c1980-2100), then foreign occupation from Europeans? or Americans? involving the destruction of mosques.

(3) Hinduism: India

1. What Happened in Hinduism and the Indian Civilisation
(a) Experience of the Fire
Iranian Fire of Mithras, and at the same time the Indo-European Sky Father of the Kurgan civilisation (later Dyaeus Pitar). Iranian-Indian Fire-god Agni. Mitra, Varuna and Indra mentioned in the *Rig Veda*. The Iranians, out of whom the early Hindus developed, knew the Fire. The Fire symbolised in fire-cult as in Iran.
(b) Growth of Hindu Religion
Iranian Fire migrated to the Indus Valley, to Mohenjo-Daro and Harappa c 1500BC, created a new religion of Hindu Vedism in the Ganges valley round gods mentioned in the *Rig Veda*: Agni, Siva (a cross-legged god) and Rudra. "Hindu" in Persian meant "the people across the River Sindhu" in Sind, Pakistan. The orthodoxy spread among many states in the Ganges valley 1000-500BC, peoples were slowly attracted to the Fire of Agni in the *Rig Veda* (p73). By 600BC Hindu Vedism had grown into Hindu Brahmanism, priestly Brahmins worshipped Brahman who was united by the Fire with the Atman (the divine part of man) - see *Upanisads* (5th century BC). Sects arose which questioned Brahmanism, notably Jainism (Mahavira's Fire c557BC) and Buddhism (the Buddha's enlightenment c525BC). India's religious development was from now on a tussle between Hindu sects (Tantric Hindu Saivism, Vaisnavism) and dissenting Jainism and Buddhism, and later (8th century AD) Vaisnavism.
(c) Consequent Growth and Development of the Indian Civilisation
The first Indian empire arose after Alexander's visit to India, the Mauryan Empire in North and Central India, modern Pakistan and Bangladesh c325BC, which was pro-Jain. At its height c250BC under Asoka, who was pro-Buddhist. 1st century AD, tussle began between Mahayana

Buddhism and Siva (see pp230-1). Military threat from Scythians, or Sakas, expansion of Gupta Empire (heyday 320-540AD) until the invasion of the Huns. Heretical sect of Islamic Allah resisted by Hindus. Decline of traditional Indian religion before the influence of Islam and the rise of Vaisnavism, resistance by Bhakti mystics. Military blow from Islamic Turks 1150, secularization and revival of interest in Turkish Islam (Arab civilisation). Turkish Ghurids won a civil war, heretical Indian Allah became the orthodoxy, expansion of Moslem/Hindu empires (13th to 16th century) until Timur, new expansion of Islamic Moghul Empire. Akbar allowed all religions to practise alongside Islam. Sikhism combined Islamic and Hindu outlooks. The Fire declined before the European threat as the Maratha Empire gave way to European influence. Conglomerate of the British Raj under foreign (British) influence 1818-1947.

2. Key Themes
1. The Fire as the central idea of Vedic Brahmanic Hinduism in relation to its Iranian origin.
2. Spread of Vedism-Brahmanism in India, peoples drawn by Fire.
3. Secularization of priestly hierarchy into an orthodox religion in India.
4. Brahmins' increasing political power.
5. Growth of a unified divine kingdom (e.g. under Asoka) linked to the Fire.
6. Temple Brahmanism pushing Indian expansion.
7. Islamic Turkish invasion of India created a revival of Arab culture.
8. Worldly Hindu priests caused a Reformation under Moslems (as erotic Tantrism and a fertility cult mixed with Brahmanism and bhakti) and more puritanical Khaljis.
9. Heretical Islam created the Moghul Empire.
10. Decline of religion associated with decolonisation before the Europeans.

11. European imperialist foreign influence, leading to new federalism under the influence of Western investment.

3. Today and Significance of the Past in relation to the Future

Conglomerate ended by Gandhi, growing Universalism as Hindu, Moslem and Christian themes united in Theosophy. Revival of Indian culture in 20th century. Gandhi's independence movement. Partition of Moslem East Pakistan and West Pakistan on religious grounds. Continuing tension between Hindus and Moslems (India-Pakistan wars) and religious tensions involving Sikhs and Tamils. The assassination of Mahatma Gandhi, Indira Gandhi and Rajiv Gandhi against the background of Hindu/Moslem, Sikh and Tamil tensions.

Independent federal India with federally linked regions under Western influence (Western investment). The Indian constitution provides for a unitary state with subsidiary federal features. Economic decline and foreign occupation ahead, c2050? India is past her best and faces a future of foreign occupation and religious decline.

(4) Buddhism: China and Japan
(Buddhism is the new religion of the South-East Asian and Tibetan civilisations. It had an impact on the Chinese and Japanese religions which began round Ti and Shintoism. Buddhism touched the Japanese civilisation more than the Chinese civilisation, which had been in existence 2000 years before the Buddha.)

1. What Happened in Buddhism
(a) Experience of the Fire
Buddha c525BC in India. Blowing out of the fire of ego and letting in of Light in enlightenment. Unlike Hinduism there is no Atman in Buddhism. Later, Mahayana sunyata and Mind Essence describe the Fire.
(b) Growth of Buddhist Religion
Indian Theravada Buddhism was about the historical

Buddha, Mahayana (1st century AD) was more metaphysical (the Buddha's celestial identity). Mahayana declined in India in the face of the Huns (6th century AD) but its schools spread eastwards along the Silk Route to Central Asia, Korea, Tibet, Java, Sumatra, Sri Lanka (Ceylon). In South-East Asia (Burma, Thailand, Vietnam, Cambodia) it attracted South-East Asian peoples 1st-4th century AD. In Tibet 200BC; attracted the Tibetan people by 608AD. In China by 300AD; Nagarjuna's school to China (5th century AD) and Japan (7th century AD). (For schools see pp 221-3.)

(c) Consequent Growth and Development of Four Civilisations

1. South-East Asia. Mon kingdoms. Mahayana Buddhism tussled with Hinduism. Military threat from Nanchao. Expansion c850-1100. Military threat from the Chams. Indianised new people adopted Theravada Buddhism. Expansion 1287-1550 and empires in Burma, Siam and Cambodia 1550-1786. Decline before the European empires. Buddhism was central to Korea from 660, but as in China Neo-Confucianism took over as the heresy in Korea.

2. Tibet. Chinese Buddhism tussled with Indian Tantric Buddhism, which won. Military threat from the Mongols. Tibetan expansion 1247-1481. The heretical sect was the Dge-lugs-pa, military threat from the Tumed Mongols, revival of Mongolian culture. The heresy of Tibetan Buddhism became orthodoxy under the Dalai Lamas, who expanded 1720-1903. Decolonisation before the Europeans (British) and Chinese.

3. China began with Ti or Shang Ti and unified 221BC under Shih Huang Ti (of the pottery army). Military threat from the Hsiung-nu (Huns). Expansion, with Buddhist Light renewing during the Golden Age of Chinese Buddhism in the T'ang period 618-907. The heretical sect was Neo-Confucianism, Buddhists were persecuted 845, Chinese religion declined before the Juchen and Mongols. Buddhism spread. Revival of interest in Arab culture (via

Mongols). The Ming new people adopted a Neo-Confucianist heresy and expanded in the Ming empire 1398-1644. The Manchus' Ch'ing 1644-1840. Decline before the Europeans, a Marxian conglomerate.

4. Japan. Japan began with Shinto Kami and unified c420 with the Yamato court. Chinese Buddhism came after c550. Military threat from the Chinese and Koreans, expansion with Buddhism as the State religion. The heretical sect was Ch'an (later Zen). Decline of religion before the Mongols and Koreans. 13th century Nichiren. Revival of pre-Mongol Chinese culture including Ch'an, the new Shogunate adopted a Zen Buddhist heresy, expansion 1573-1863, with Buddhism an arm of government. Decline of Zen Buddhist religion before the Europeans and Shinto. Decolonisation before the Americans. The American occupation.

2. Key Themes

1. The Fire as the central idea of Buddhism in South-East Asia and Tibet, in relation to its Indian origin.

2. Spread of Buddhism among South-East Asian and Tibetan peoples, drawn by the Fire.

3. Secularization of Buddhism into the State in South-East Asia and Tibet, and Japan (where Buddhism was the State religion).

4. Buddhist monks' increasing political power.

5. Growth of a unified divine kingdom through Buddhism in South-East Asia, Tibet and Japan.

6. Buddhism pushing expansion of the South-East Asian and Tibetan civilisations.

7. Indianised Cham attacks on South-East Asia and Mongol attacks on Tibet, China and Japan created revivals of Indian, Central Asian, Arab and pre-Mongol Chinese culture in South-East Asia.

8. Worldly Buddhist monks caused a Reformation under Indian and Burmese Theravada Buddhism in South-East Asia and Dalai Lamas in Tibet and under more puritanical sects.

9. Heretical Theravada Buddhism, the Dalai Lamas'

Tibetan Buddhism and Zen Buddhism created empires in South-East Asia, Tibet and Japan.
10. Decline of religion associated with decolonisation before the Europeans.
11. European imperialist foreign influence and new federation in South-East Asia.
12. China and Tibet are still under a Communist conglomerate, Japan is still under an American-influenced conglomerate; federalism is ahead for all four civilisations where Buddhism has taken root.

3. Today and Significance of the Past in relation to the Future
Buddhism is the main religion in Tibet and South-East Asia; but second to Shinto in Japan and a foreign intrusion in China (almost like the Saddam Hussein mosque in Britain).
1. South-East Asia. European empires ended, coming federation of South-East Asian states (Pacific Community).
2. Tibet. The Dalai Lama is in exile. Communist Chinese occupation in Tibet. Revival of Tibetan culture. Tibet will join a coming federation of South-East Asian states (Pacific Community).
3. China. Chinese are still under Communism. The Red Guards' persecution. Confucianism, Taoism and Chinese Buddhism will re-emerge and draw together, there will be a return of Confucianism and a federalist post-Communist China with regions breaking up c2020? (Compare the CIS following the U.S.S.R.)
4. Japan. American occupation began a conglomerate with loss of national sovereignty (American constitution with no war clause). Economic success. Drawing together of Shinto, Buddhism and Christianity. Shinto now co-exists with Buddhism, modern Soka-gakkai (Nichiren). Return to Shinto Fire-based culture which began at Hirohito's funeral. Coming federation as Japan breaks up into regions (islands?) within a Pacific Community? Will it be linked to China and South-East Asia within an American-led world

APPENDIX

government?
Japan may have economic strength but it is older than
America. America will eventually incorporate Japan, not the
other way round, despite the image of Bush being cradled
in the Japan PM's lap.
Comparing China with Japan. China is a nuclear power
but is relatively economically backward. Japan has a smaller
population but greater economic might. Both are in the same
phase of advancement though China has greater antiquity.
The possibility that Japan will form a Pacific Community
that includes South-East Asia, Oceania, China and Tibet. If
so Buddhism's importance will grow.

(5) Orthodox Christianity: Russian Empire

1. What Happened in Orthodox Christianity and the
Byzantine-Russian Civilisation
(a) Experience of the Fire
   The transfiguration of Christ from the Israelite
civilisation. Early Christians went to Britain and Rome,
where Christianity became the State religion under
Constantine. Founding of Byzantium 330. The Byzantine
tradition, Desert Fathers in Egypt, Syria and Palestine (4th-
5th century) (see pp 139-141), rebelling against the worldly
alliance of Church and State under Constantine and seeking
the Fire or Light. Orthodox monasticism emphasising the
transfiguration.
(b) Growth of Orthodox Religion
   The Roman Fire migrated to Byzantium in once Hittite
Anatolia, and created Greek Orthodox religion c395 when
the Roman Empire split into East and West, Byzantine
people were attracted to the Eastern approach and the
Byzantine occupation of Greece began. After the dissolution
of the Western Empire (476) Eastern Monophysitism (the
doctrine that Christ has one nature that is divine and human)
versus Rome. Iconoclasm. Schism, heresy based on
Moscow. Splits of 867 and 1054 between Eastern Greek
and Western Latin Christianity. Decline of Byzantine

151

religion before the Crusaders, Venetian Latins and Turks. The heresy of the Russian Orthodox Christ adopted by the Grand Duchy of Moscow. Suppression of religion under secularizing Communism.

(c) Consequent Growth and Development of the Byzantine-Russian Civilisation

Unification of Justinian's empire c540. Military threat of the Persians, Avars and Arabs. Expansion c677-1071. The heretical sect of Byzantine Christ of Moscow as the third Rome from c988, decline of religion before the Crusaders, Venetian Latins and Turks 1071-1354. Heresy resisted by Venetian Latins, Byzantine mystics and Hesychasts. Military threat from the Ottomans, revival of Italian Rome by the Russian Grand Duchy of Moscow which adopted the heretical Christ of the third Rome as the new orthodoxy, Russian Orthodox Christ. Expansion 1462-1689 and again 1689-1853. Religion declined before the European influence, decolonisation before Western Marxism. Communist conglomerate 1918-1991, which suppressed religion.

2. Key Themes

1. The Fire as the central idea of Greek/Eastern Orthodox religion in relation to its origin in Roman Christianity.
2. Spread of Eastern Orthodox religion into Byzantine territories.
3. Secularization of Orthodox religion after 451.
4. Eastern Orthodox's increasing political power after the dissolution of the West Roman empire in 476.
5. Growth of a unified empire under Justinian, linked to the Fire.
6. Orthodox Christianity pushing Byzantine expansion.
7. Ottoman capture of Constantinople created a revival of Italian European culture in Moscow.
8. Worldly Byzantine patriarchs during the Crusades caused a Reformation under the Grand Duchy of Moscow.
9. Heretical Moscow created the Russian Empire.

10. Decline of religion associated with decolonisation before the Europeans.
11. European-influenced Communist conglomerate, leading to the CIS and eventually a new federalism under the influence of Western investment.

3. Today and Significance of the Past in relation to the Future

The end of the Soviet conglomerate (U.S.S.R.), and its transfer to federalism is now happening via the CIS. Universalism of Orthodox, Catholic and Protestant Christianity. Revival of the Russian Byzantine Fire-based tradition, i.e. the revival of the Orthodox Church which can be seen today in Moscow. A Federalist post-Communist Russia will be linked to the coming United States of Europe.

The Byzantine-Russian civilisation is older than the European civilisation, so could not have conquered Europe. A law that older civilisations do not conquer younger ones, whereas younger ones do conquer older ones.

The southern ex-Soviet Moslem states may break away and form a Moslem confederation with other Moslem states. Between them they will have nuclear weapons.Russia/CIS to ally with the U.S. and Europe against Islam.

(6) Christianity: Europe and America

1. What Happened in Christianity and the European and North American Civilisations

(a) Experience of the Fire

The transfiguration of Christ, the possibly Essene Light of the World. St Paul (the vision on the road to Damascus) and early Christians under Joseph of Arimathaea, who spread the Fire from the Israelite civilisation to the Celtic and Roman civilisations. Later the Fire or Light of Christ, St Augustine and Pope Gregory the Great.

(b) Growth of Christian Religion

Joseph of Arimathaea went to France and Britain.

Caractacus was taken from Britain to Rome. Christianity spread in Rome and was finally adopted as the State religion in Rome under Constantine in c312, accelerating the Roman civilisation's decline. Roman churches, the mission to Celtic Britain, Christianity was adopted by the descendants of the Teutonic Germanic-Scandinavian barbarians who overthrew the Roman Empire in France, Germany and Italy, and established Arian kingdoms. The rise of the new religion in 5th-6th century Europe, which attracted Teutonic barbarians (for conversion dates see p513, no. 14) and inspired stones. Charlemagne's Holy Roman Empire. Growth in power of the Catholic church and Popes through the Crusades. Increased worldliness of the Church led to the Protestant Reformation. Protestant individualism led to American Evangelical Protestantism. Decline of religion in Europe and decolonisation.

(c) Consequent Growth and Development of the European and North American Civilisations

Schism between Western Christ and Eastern Orthodox Christ over the Fire, military threat from the Vikings, Spanish Moslems and Magyars. Europe's anti-Moslem expansion into Italy, Sicily, Spain and the Crusader states 951-1244 linked with Jerusalem and the Fire. The heresy of the Templars, Cathars, Lollards and Hussites who, with the Fire-renewing 14th century mystics, opposed the decline of the Christian religion before the Mongol and Arab advances. Military blow: the shock of the Moslem Ottoman victory in Byzantine Constantinople led to a secular response of the Holy Roman State and to the Renaissance, a revival of interest in Greece and Rome as the libraries of Constantinople came to Rome. The Reformation and civil war (Spanish Catholicism v German Protestantism). Emergence of the heresy of Protestantism under a new people (the Humanists), individualism, expansion into Mercantile Empire and American colonies (1555-1778), the rise and defeat of Puritanism, the Industrial Revolution, Romanticism. Further expansion into empire (1778-1914), anti-colonialists in Africa, India, and Asia who secularized

APPENDIX

and cosmopolitanised from 1880. Breakdown of certainties with the First World War, religion weakened before scepticism, decline of the European empires before the Americans. Meanwhile, the Fire of the American civilisation grew out of the European civilisation. The Christian Fire from before 1494 to 1650 and new non-Catholic Protestantism/ Puritanism in the North-East American colonies attracted the North American peoples, who built stones. The Great Awakening (Protestant revivalism), independence, the creation of the United States' federal constitution. Evangelical American Protestantism, military blow as the Confederacy seceded. Expansion from 1913 to present.

2. Key Themes
  1. The Fire as the central idea of Christianity in relation to its Israelite origin.
  2. Spread of Christianity among Romanised Teutonic Germanic barbarians drawn by the Fire.
  3. Secularization of church into State in the former barbarian kingdoms.
  4. Roman Popes' increasing political power.
  5. Birth and growth of the Holy Roman Empire from c800, linked to the Fire.
  6. Christianity pushing European expansion through the Crusades - the Fire of St Bernard.
  7. Moslem conquest of Constantinople created the Renaissance.
  8. Worldly Popes caused the Reformation under the Protestants and more puritanical Puritans.
  9. Heretical Protestantism created European empires.
  10. Decline of religion associated with decolonisation.

3. Today and Significance of the Past in relation to the Future
  European decolonisation after conflict with the American and Russian empires, final triumph of American ideology. A conglomerate ahead, an American-backed United States

of Europe (a union, not a federation), growing syncretism (of Christianity and New Age cults) and Universalism. There will be a return to the Fire-based medieval vision in a new Baroque movement and then a Federalism (of independent nation-states) after 2150. Europe can expect to last to c2725 AD. Declining Christian religion, with only 2.5% churchgoing, and declining prospects, like Greece when over the hill.

The American expansion after two world wars, now poised for a world role until c2250? Compare Rome after two Punic wars. Growing Universalism, a heresy which can become the orthodoxy. America is young, compare young Byzantium and old Rome. The energetic American religion, 60% go to church, and a positive global outlook, like Rome after the two Punic Wars.

End

We have seen that the Fire is what all the religions and civilisations have in common. A coming world-wide civilisation can draw on the unity of the Fire in religions. The Fire is present within all world conflicts and offers common ground to: Catholics and Protestants in Northern Ireland, Hindus and Moslems, and Moslems and Jews, all of whom share the Fire. Closing theme linked to coming European union and global harmony.

4. TEN RELIGIONS IN RELATION TO THEIR CIVILISATIONS

(These notes are of interest as they identify the most important events in ten civilisations in relation to their religions, and give further practical expression to the idea of Universalism as the essence of all religions. Page numbers refer to key passages in *The Fire and the Stones*.)

(1) Egyptian Religion
Now: Suez, Nasser, Saddat, Moslem Brotherhood. Islam.
Story: a religion of the akh and divine Pharaoh becoming humanised and dying out.

APPENDIX

1. Pyramids, Khufu, obsession with becoming an akh, temple-pictures.
2. Hyksos invaders from Canaan, become a new people in Thebes, the humanising of Pharaoh, Amun, Akhenaton and Aton, Tutankhamun.
3. End of Egyptian civilisation: Persians, Alexander, Byzantines, Islam 642.
Theme: metaphysical vision at start, secularized at end. Religion of the akh acted as thruster of civilisation, which petered out as the akh was superseded by foreign occupation.

(2) Islam
Now: Fundamentalism, Teheran suggesting a federation of southern ex-Soviet Moslem states.
Story: a new religion creating a thrusting empire, conquest of land for the Prophet; resurgence of religion after Western secularization.
1. Mohammed, the Fire and the *Koran* and Empire; blasphemy and the execution of Bayazid and Al-Hallaj. Suhrawardi's execution?
2. Mongol attack on Baghdad 1258.
3. Rise of the Ottomans, a new people, and the fall of Constantinople 1453.
4. End of the Ottoman Empire, T.E. Lawrence's role in this, Western rule in Islam and the resurgence of Fundamentalism which is anti-Western.
Theme: Religion of fana thrusting the civilisation into empire and resistance to the Crusaders, turning theosophical under the Mongols and Turks, still vital despite Western rule.

(3) Hinduism
Now: Mahatma Gandhi, Indira and Rajiv. India and Pakistan, Sikhs, Tamils.
Story: Hindu tolerance, surviving challenges from Buddhism and Moslems.
1. Hindus arriving from Iran c1500BC; Vedism.

2. Challenge to Brahmanism of Buddhism and Jainism; Asoka's tolerant Mauryan Empire.

3. Arrival of the Moslems, the new people, and Akbar's Moghul Empire.

4. The British Raj, Gandhi, and the resurgence of Hinduism in independence.

Theme: The 4,000 year long endurance of the Hindu religion of the Atman which inspired challenges and empires, and even the British Raj. Unavoidable parallels with Islam under Western rule.

(4) China: Ti and Confucianism

Now: China under Mao, Cultural Revolution, the crushing of the democracy movement.

Story: the survival of the central Chinese religious idea despite alternatives.

1. Shang Ti and the emperor Shih Huang Ti of the pottery army, who unified China and worked on Great Wall of China which kept out the Hsiung-nu (Huns). Confucius.

2. Taoism and the arrival of Buddhism (pp 239-40). Neo-Taoism 3rd-4th century AD, and the persecution of Buddhism in 845. Neo-Confucianist restatement of Ti.

3. Mongol conquest of China c1271.

4. Ming ("Brightness") new people and Neo-Confucianism's return.

5. End of the Emperors, the last Emperor a gardener (Henry Pu Yi), Chiang Kai Shek's Kuomintang, Communism and the Cultural Revolution. Will Neo-Confucianism return?

Theme: The survival of Ti in a different form, through Confucianism. Religion of inner brightness which thrust China into unity (p428, 425).

(5) Japan: Shintoism

Now: Wartime Japan, Japan now a trading giant, the richest country in the world.

Story: A tussle between two religions.

1. Shinto beginning, the Yamato court unifying the

country under tenno (Emperor of Heaven) (663, p433); then imitating China and importing Buddhism to be the State religion. Emperors, Kyoto. Reconstruct from old buildings.

2. Mongol invasions 1274 and 1281, and kamikaze (divine wind) saved Japan.

3. New Ashikaga shogunate and Zen Buddhism.

4. Revival of Shintoism before Second World War, divine Emperor, war, Hiroshima, American occupation under MacArthur. Shinto revival at Hirohito's funeral.

Theme: Shinto as the backbone of Japanese civilisation despite spells of dominance by Buddhism.

(6) Orthodox

Now: Russian Orthodox services in Moscow attended by Yeltsin, Cold War ended.

Story: Orthodoxy based on the Christian transfiguration gave thrust to the expansion of the Byzantine Empire and later of the Russian Empire.

1. The founding of Byzantium 330AD, separation from West Roman Empire. The Byzantine Empire under Justinian; Greek culture fighting off invaders (Persians, Avars, Arabs), expansion under the Emperor of East.

2. Ottoman attack on Constantinople 1453, the imperial family fled to Moscow and married into the Russian Duchy of Moscow. Christ of third Rome (i.e. Moscow).

3. Triumph of the Westernisers. Peter the Great, Communism, Cold War. Now pro-Western Yeltsin. But Slavophile Russian Orthodox tradition still strong and resurgent.

Theme: Orthodoxy inspired two regions.

(7) Christianity

Now: Decolonisation of the European empires after Second World War, America dominant e.g. precision bombing in Gulf War, space rockets.

Story: The rise and decline of Europe, the rise of America.

1. The crucifixion, the Garden Tomb, Joseph of

Arimathaea bringing Christianity to Britain, thence Christianity to Rome where it took over the Roman Empire under Constantine and was adopted by Germanic tribes and inspired Charlemagne's unification.

2. European expansion. The Crusades.

3. The Protestants, the new people, and the Reformation, and two empires.

4. Persecution of the Puritans, the Mayflower, America's independence.

5. How two World Wars were won by America and ruined Europe, leading to decolonisation and a secularized Christianity in the 20th century.

Theme: Christianity inspired the unification of Europe and the United States of America. Lack of Christianity was accompanied by European decolonisation. A civilisation needs a belief to feel confidence.

(8) Buddhism

Now: South-East Asia is in post-European vacuum, partly occupied by Communism.

Story: how Mahayana Buddhism turned Theravada.

1. Spread of Mahayana Buddhism after 1st century AD.

2. Angkor Wat in Cambodia which changed from Hinduism to Mahayana in the 12th century AD (pp 237-8).

3. Indianised new people adopt Theravada.

4. Arrival of the Europeans, the survival of Buddhism.

Theme: regional differences but sameness of Buddhist inspiration for South-East Asian civilisation. Include the Easter Island giants (Buddhas)?

(9) Tibetan Buddhism

Now: Tibet under Chinese occupation, the Dalai Lama in exile.

Story: The development of a new kind of (Tantric) Buddhism.

1. Indian Tantric Buddhism into Tibet.

2. Mongolia forced Tibet to be a vassal to Genghis Khan c1207.

APPENDIX

3. The Dalai Lamas took over from 1409.
4. The Dalai Lama in exile. Chinese cultural rape in the Cultural Revolution. Destruction of Lhasa monasteries, but survival of Tibetan Buddhism.
Theme: uncrushable Tibetan Buddhism, how Tibet's home-grown kind of Buddhism inspired Tibet's expansion and was adopted by mighty Mongolia of the Central Asian civilisation.

(10) Judaism
Now: Israel and Palestine, West bank. Terrorism.
Story: Monotheism of Yahweh.
1. Abraham came from Ur, first Hebrews came from Sumeria.
2. Moses came from Egypt (where he had encountered Aton) to the Promised Land, his covenant with Yahweh. David.
3. Assyrians dispersed Israel. Jews of Judah, a new people. First and Second Temple.
4. Roman sack of Masada and eventual absorption of Israel into Arab civilisation, 636.
Theme: Yahweh inspired the Israelite civilisation until foreign conquest.

Civilisations not used:

Indo-European	Germanic-Scandinavian:
Iranian: Zoroastrianism	Vikings
Mesopotamian: Babylon	Andean
Celtic: Druids	Meso-American: Aztecs
Greek	and Incas
Roman	African
Anatolian: Hittites	Oceanian
Syrian	Central Asian

The television outcome of these four approaches to *The Fire and the Stones* is at present still unknown, but they have already evoked a good guide to Nicholas Hagger's thinking from four different angles.

APPENDIX 2

THE ORIGIN AND CREATION OF THE UNIVERSE:
A FORM FROM MOVEMENT THEORY

On page 111 Nicholas Hagger wrote of the "origin of the universe: seeing the hot beginning (Big Bang) in relation to the metaphysical reality of the Fire or Light". At the Cambridge symposium for which he wrote the third essay (see page 95), he had discussions with a Norwegian mathematician as a result of which he proposed a Form from Movement Theory regarding the origin of the universe. The following is a relatively early version of this theory (dated late September 1992) which adds flesh to point 1 on page 111.

Precisely how did the creation of the universe take place? An underlying assumption of many theories and ideas of creation is that stillness and simplicity are basic, and that movement and complexity somehow arise from this basic condition. In contrast, we may begin with infinite movement and complexity as an ontological basic condition, and assert that manifestation is a reduction or limitation of this, rather than some additional quality. I propose a first principle that is an eternal and infinite movement of what might be termed the metaphysical Fire or Light, and following a discussion with the Norwegian mathematician Henning Bråten, I offer these embryonic concepts for exploration and dialogue, with the aim of generating further clarification and analogous proposals.

Although the creation was one undivided process, we can, for the purpose of considering it in thought, treat it as happening in four relatively (but not rigidly) distinct stages which can be termed (in increasing order of manifestation) Nothingness, Non-Being, Being and Existence. I assume that this creation is an unfolding event within what I have termed the Fire or Light, and the four stages of the manifestation of the universe are as follows:

APPENDIX

1. There is a completely self-entangled energy of (virtual or actual) infinite movement in all directions which we call Nothingness. (We may also call it real nothing or Oneness and think of it as the metaphysical Fire or Light.) I postulate that this Nothingness is, in a primitive sense, infinitely self-aware. (As it is infinitely and inexhaustibly complex in every sense, Gödel/Turing-inspired postulates that no finitely generated system is capable of complete self-understanding are not applicable.) In the language of modern physics we might say that we begin with non-locality, and derive locality from this as a special case. We thus begin with an infinite movement (compare the thinking of Henrik Tschudi), which we formally denote as M. M is absolutely the most subtle substance.

2. All kinds of limitations of M are potentialities within M, each of which corresponds to a certain kind of creation. We postulate that in a certain (infinite) region of M, which can be denoted as S, a limitation of movement occurs so that we get a regular movement, possibly in the form of a multidimensional spiral. The idea is that this regular movement arises as all irregular movement in this region dies away. S, or Non-Being, can be said to be a subset of M, where both M and S are infinite. Everything in M not in S is denoted M-S (M minus S). Thus in place of Oneness we now have a certain fundamental duality, that of M-S versus S. (Or pre-manifestation and first manifestation.) Whereas M-S is thought of as entailing all sorts of infinitely complex movement, S is in contrast a fairly simple and symmetrical form of movement. As in set theory, both M and S are infinite, yet M is larger than S and contains the whole of S. In the same way, there is a more definite but still infinite self-entanglement (non-locality) in all of S.

Clearly there will be a kind of creative tension between M-S and S. (Compare Ilya Prigogine's work on the interplay between regularity and randomness.) This may result in new forms of order arising between M-S and S, as a result of their "interplay".

One such possible order is that of symmetric points or

"pre-particles". We postulate that a pair of pre-particles arises in S as a result of the pressure of M-S on S. These pre-particles, which can be termed +p and -p, are symmetrically entangled and are opposite or complementary in most senses. We can put this succinctly by saying that in sum they equal zero (in S: +p + -p = 0).

3. We now postulate a certain reduction of symmetry by virtue of the disturbing influence of the infinitely complex (and "chaotic") movement of M-S upon S. This manifests at first as an annihilation of one of the pre-particles, say -p. An "annihilation" in this context means that the regular movement constituting a pre-particle is absorbed into the vast movement of M. The symmetry is broken in that the other pre-particle,+p, is not absorbed into M but derives energy from the movement of M-S upon S. This empty point is a vacuum (compare Dante's "infinitesimal point") or singularity (compare Roger Penrose's singularity). This point potentially contains Non-Being. We can say that this point is "a defined Non-Being" in contrast to the undefined Non-Being which is S, and both aspects of Non-Being were always potentials within the unmanifest Fire or Light, i.e. M (see 1). This point, +p, begins to spread like a multidimensional wave in all directions in the field of S and expands. (Compare the work of Edgard Gunzig on virtual particles.) One of the pre-particles is gradually becoming Being, the first subtle structure in the vacuum field of S: +p —> B. Thus we can say: from Non-Being happens Being.

What we are postulating here is that, due to the interplay between itself and M-S in the field of S, B is evolving more and more structure (compare Prigogine's ideas). We see M-S as a source of infinitely complex impulses, more or less like a self-aware, primitively intelligent, apparently random (though perhaps fundamentally purposive) generator. S, in contrast, provides a background of "silence and space" within which the reverberations of the structure can unfold (i.e. can be displayed within M) without disturbance.

We are postulating that all this is still at the implicate

level (see David Bohm's work for a description of implicate and explicate orders and their paired dynamic relationship in a holomovement). In the language of physics we can say that the emergence from Nothingness (M) of Non-Being (the vacuum field of S) and then Being (B within S) is the activity within the quantum vacuum. Through its interaction between itself and M-S, B evolves more and more explicate orders or levels of existence (but these are still implicate when seen from the level of human beings). We can denote this series of more and more explicate implicate orders (which B contains) by $I_1, I_2, I_3,...,I_n$; where I_n corresponds to the most explicate order that is still implicate to us.

4. Obviously we then denote Existence or the explicate order (E) by I_{n+1}. And we can say that $E = I_{n+1}$, which is an event in M. The process of Being (formerly +p) becoming Existence is one in which potentialities become actualities, pre-particles become particles, pre-matter becomes matter, pre-organisms become organisms, pre-consciousness becomes consciousness and possibility becomes actuality, completing the process of manifestation. As in Bohm's work, we can postulate the possibility that there are one or more loops between these, such as between I_{n+1} and I_{n-2} (the explicate order and the third implicate order). These provide the rudiments of a primitive consciousness enfolded within matter. There is also a possibility that there is a certain "horizontal" division into two unfolding orders, one eventually leading up to explicate matter and the other eventually leading up to aware consciousness and creative intelligence, with one or more "vertical" bridges between the two streams.

As a result of +p deriving energy from M-S, the infinite and implicate +p or Being, which has spread in all directions in the field of S and expanded, has become pre-matter (and as we have just seen, perhaps also pre-consciousness) in place of a first pre-proton (+p), and form is ready to arise from the infinite movement. Virtual particles emerge from the quantum vacuum (B in the field of S) in pairs, and one particle in each pair has the potentiality to become a real particle in explicate Existence if it draws energy from the pressure of M-S on S. (Compare Edgard Gunzig's work on virtual particles.) Through quantum processes, the emergence of virtual particles happens in many regions of S, all over the expanded field of +p or B, and, deriving energy from the pressure of M-S on S, many ephemeral virtual particles become enduring real particles. As a result of the proliferation of simultaneously emerging real particles, the process of the Big Bang or hot beginning (or many big bangs), the actual creation of the universe as we know it, takes place. Space-time can be seen in terms of events, and according to the anti-Newtonian Leibniz (second letter to Clarke) space is an order of co-existence of events and time an order of succession of events. However, the notion of "event" has to be clarified in our context. The thinking of the Leibnizian Geoffrey Read may be of help.

The process of the origin and creation of the universe - of manifestation - can be summarised mathematically as follows: $M \longrightarrow M\text{-}S + S$. In S, $+p + \text{-}p = 0$. In S, $+p \longrightarrow B$, which evolves $I_1, I_2, I_3,...I_n$. $B \longrightarrow E$, which is I_{n+1}.

Clearly there is a certain kind of arbitrariness in that, in a word, *anything* may happen when we begin with infinite movement and self-entanglement, and the process here indicated is merely one of infinitely many possible processes. In particular, many conditions will have to be fulfilled for such events to lead to something resembling the manifest universe.

If we begin with visualisations of what is going on, not only at the explicate levels (as in modern physics) but also at the ultimate levels (as in mathematically and poetically inspired ideas of creation), these visualisations may be "co-evolutionary" in the sense that they nurture each other, as if building a bridge from both sides of a gap simultaneously. Such informal ideas can then be formalised and compared with ideas derived (as interpretation) from actual measurements. This mutual interplay in and between our minds can correspond very roughly to this ultimate interplay that we are considering.[1]

APPENDIX 3

BEYOND EVOLUTION AND NEURONS: MANIFESTATION AND TRANSMISSIVE CONSCIOUSNESS

This essay sharpens points 5 and 9 on pages 111-2. The Cambridge Symposium on reductionism, for which the paper on page 95 was written, proved to be dominated by materialists and, disenchanted with the prevailing ethos, Nicholas Hagger was stirred into formulating the following alternative to materialism. Most of the neuroscientists and materialists named took part, and quotations not attributed in the Notes are taken from their contributions.

Evolution has become a generally accepted theory. This is of course mainly the result of the work of Darwin, who sailed as an unpaid naturalist on the HMS Beagle in 1831 and from 1856 wrote an account of evolution, delivering a joint paper with Wallace in 1858. Darwinism is Darwin's theory of the evolutionary mechanism that explains gradual organic change, and it sees the process of evolution as working through heredity, variation and the struggle for existence or survival, which relates varieties to their environments and alters species through selective reproduction or natural selection. As he wrote in his *Autobiography* of the principle of natural selection, in the course of the struggle for existence "favourable variations would tend to be preserved, and unfavourable ones to be destroyed....The result of this would be the formation of new species." Darwinism sees advanced forms including "homo sapiens" as evolving by blind chance; complex and successful life forms are thrown up by random mutations, and in *The Descent of Man* (1871) Darwin expanded on the evolution of man from the ape and saw moral, spiritual, psychological and physiological traits as arising by evolution from the great apes.

Neo-Darwinism has purged Darwinism of Darwin's

167

support for Lamarck's theory of the inheritance of acquired characteristics, for Darwinism was wrong about inheritance. Neo-Darwinists distinguish bodily variation that is not inheritable from variation which can be inherited.

Darwin's evidence was his geological observation, his collection of specimens between 1830 and 1839 and his speculations in his private notebooks about "the species problem" which are based on specimens he had collected during his voyage. Through observation he had arrived at a branching tree of species by 1842; he provided a longer version in 1844, and then digressed into barnacles until Wallace came out with the theory he himself had been working on for 20 years. The joint paper with Wallace was arranged by Darwin's friends Lyell, Hooker and the reductionist T.H. Huxley.

Today neo-Darwinism is reaffirmed in the books of Richard Dawkins, such as *The Blind Watchmaker*, but Darwinism remains a theory. It has not been proved in a laboratory, and no-one has found a part-human, part-ape fossil or skull. The discovery in 1912 of the Piltdown skull turned out to be a forgery, and Dr Leakey's fossils and skulls from Africa are of apes rather than men. (His discovery in 1948 of Proconsul africanus from 25 million years ago, and in 1962 of Kenyapithecus from 14 million years ago, proposed ancestors to humans and apes, and his discovery in 1960-3 of homo habilis in Tanzania is claimed to be an evolutionary link between homo erectus, the direct ancestor to homo sapiens, and the australopithecus africanus who became extinct over 2 million years ago.) A recent theory that apes took to the water and that man evolved from aquatic apes cites a tiny bone in man's ear canal but otherwise there is no evidence. A 250,000 year old large-brained skull has been discovered at Atapuerca, N. Spain, suggesting that large-brained man is longer established in Europe than has been previously thought. Richard Milton in *The Facts of Life: Shattering the Myth of Darwinism* challenges neo-Darwinism from geological, archaeological and biological observations, some of which fly in the face of received cosmology, geology, history and architecture; notably his contention that the earth is only around 170,000 years old rather than 4.5 billion years old, or, according to Prof. Harry Butcher's new dating method, half the age previously thought. The American biologist Stephen Jay Gould has described in *Wonderful Life* how in the Burgess Shale in Canada well-adapted marine fossils just disappeared, suggesting that evolution is the survival not of the fittest but of the luckiest - or of the intended.

*

Neo-Darwinism has recently joined forces with neuroscience, which focuses on the mind-brain problem from the position of neural materialism, and the Nobel prize-winner Gerald Edelman has brought out a book with the title *Neural Darwinism.*

Neural materialism asserts that the neuron is the unit of brain-function and therefore of mind and memory, and that it was thrown up by chance through evolution. Neurons or nerve cells are the basic cells of the nervous system in vertebrates and most invertebrates, and impulses are carried into their nucleus by dendrites and out by axons (both of which are fibres), and clusters of these neurons form nerves. Focusing on the neurons has given rise to neurobiology, in which emphasis is given to the connections between neurons and to "binding", and this has led neural materialists such as Steven Rose (author of *The Making of Memory*) and Michael Sofroniew to conclude that consciousness is a purely biological process and that mind is "bits of brain function"; a reductionist position. Such neurobiologists draw strength from the neurophilosophy of the American materialist philosopher Patricia Churchland, whose *Neurophilosophy* asserts that neurobiological facts about neurons explain many psychological phenomena so that psychology reduces to neuroscience. The reduction is from the macro level to the micro level, just as optics has been reduced to electromagnetic radiation. Churchland focuses on the neural basis of sensory awareness, using imaging techniques such as PET (Positron-Emission Tomography) scanners and NMR (Nuclear Magnetic Radiation) imaging. Her conclusion is that cognitive theory is to be seen in terms of neuroscience and neurons, and mental states are reducible to neurobiological states. As an instance of the effects of such a neural materialist view on philosophy, Patricia Churchland writes that Plato's view is "a desperate one" and that Plato is "the archetypal anti-naturalist", to be contrasted with "naturalists who argue that the mind is the brain".[2] Churchland is scathing about "metaphysical nay-saying" to materialism, of which Plato is an example. Darwin, on the other hand, Churchland says, wrought a revolution in biology which "makes it possible to have a genuine" (i.e. materialistic) "science of biology".

Neural Darwinism (Edelman's phrase) suggests that the mind arose at a definite time in history and evolved through connections of neurons in response to experience, with the result that biology is the key to understanding the brain. If, as Whitehead said he did, in the course of inventing mathematical physics Galileo took mind out of Nature by making the scientist an objective observer, then Edelman claims to have put the mind back into Nature again not by relating the intuition to a whole but by reducing the mind to neural connections and patterns, and binding. The brain is not a computer but a biological phenomenon whose groupings of the 10 billion neurons in each brain allow it individuality, learning and memory, and Edelman and his colleagues have built a robot, Darwin III (and more recently Darwin IV) to simulate perceptual categorisation: a perception machine that behaves like a slow animal.

Twenty disciplines contribute to the materialistic revolution in the neurosciences, which has combined Mendelian heredity and genetics together with Darwin's natural selection, and Crick's DNA (in which behaviour is programmed or coded) to make a modern synthesis of neo-Darwinism. Edelman says that Darwin's theory of natural selection "deals a death blow" to the idea that "essences" of species exist before particular organisms or exemplars do, an idea "most clearly formulated by Plato", and that Plato's essentialism is "false".[3]

As materialists go, Edelman is a moderate. He concedes that his theory is yet to be tested and he is quick to pay tribute to poetry and the imagination; the soul is our individuality, he says, but is "no longer immortal". If you ask some more extreme reductionist neurobiologists where creativity is in their neurons, they will reply, "It isn't, we haven't got that far yet," while at the same time re-emphasising that mind is just bits of brain functioning. The most extreme view is typified by P.W. Atkins: as a result of the Second Law of Thermodynamics everything is running down, we are living on a "dunghill of purposeless interconnected corruption", everything is "bleak" and "barren", nothing survives death and there is no religious truth. It is a Beckettian vision of a passive consciousness accepting that humans can be reduced to the status of evolutionary apes with a neural consciousness whose nobility consists in seeing how terrible and dreadful the world around us is (in contrast to the Romantic poets' view of it). Such a bleakness is reinforced by neurobiology, neuropsychology, neurology and neurophilosophy, and some of the young Cambridge philosophy dons take pride along with Jeremy Butterfield in announcing publicly, "I am an atheistic philosophical materialist".

The neo-Darwinian neural materialists reduce the mind-body or mind-brain dualism we have inherited from Descartes to one unified body-based physicalist reality. Unification is a worthy goal, provided it is gone about in the right way and does not exclude higher reality. However, the materialists' reduction of mental states to physical states seeks to unify the universe in terms of biology, with the result that philosophy and psychology are reduced to Darwin's biology. Plato is widely dismissed as anti-materialist, essentialist, wrong and false; and higher reality comes out in the wash.

There is some evidence that species do evolve and there is some evidence that some mental states have physiological counterparts in the brain. Where the materialists are wrong is in concluding on inadequate foundations that the evolution of species has taken place as a result of blind chance and accident and that mutations are random on a "dunghill" of a world; that human consciousness originated in the gaze of a wordless ape; and that our minds are simply the fortuitous and accidental combinations of connecting and binding neurons. These mechanistic conclusions do not follow from the materialists' premises: they are hunches, but at bottom are not founded on evidence, for very little is known about evolution in the past and evolution is not observable in the present. These mechanistic conclusions are to be regarded as unproved scientific hypotheses, for there is no evidence that (1) evolution is a matter of chance; that (2) our philosophical concepts evolved by chance from the outlook of apes; and that (3) these thoughts are simply connecting neurons which might just as well, had accident turned things out differently, have been wordless cells. If Darwin was wrong about inheritance, having no knowledge of 20th century genetic mechanisms, could he not have been wrong in seeing evolution in terms of mechanistic and random mutations, having no knowledge of any non-materialist approach?

*

The great weakness of Darwinism and neuroscience as theories is that they approach physical reality with the reason's rational theorising, which sees particulars and differences and meaninglessness, rather than with the intuitional contemplation of the soul or universal being, which (as in the case of the Romantic poets) "perceives" universals and unity and meaning in relation to an invisible reality. The reason, approaching the whole, focuses on the parts, emphasising reductionism and dismissing holism as unattainable mysticism (which to it is merely a rational, theoretical idea). As I argued in my paper on reductionism (see page 95), when the contemplative soul or universal being intuitionally contemplates the whole, it perceives it and knows it as a Universalist, metaphysical reality.

An alternative biology to Darwinism and neural materialism sees evolution in terms of the metaphysical, Universalist whole that is beyond the natural world (see page 100), and is a consequence of the Form from Movement theory I have proposed (see Appendix 2). Such a biology is manifestational. In other words, manifestation is the key to understanding how forms emerge from the movement of the metaphysical Fire or Light, and just as the germs of galaxies came out of a point from the spiral of M-S (see Appendix 2), so too did organisms. Just as the universe of galaxies expanded from a first proton (see Appendix 2), so the universe of organisms "expanded" into ascending hierarchical wholes from one organism (see page 98). This "expansion" happened as the universal energy flowed into the universal being of all organisms (see page 102), perhaps via carrier photons, and drove them to evolve from Being by creating and developing self-organising biological mechanisms in Existence. (In the same way the universe of civilisations "expanded" from a first vision of the Fire or Light, and similarly ascended through hierarchical wholes, see *The Fire and the Stones*.)

Universalist manifestation thus describes the creative drive of each organism to higher and higher levels of organism and hierarchical whole, and the invisible energy teleologically thrusts each organism in the direction its purpose requires, driving it to adapt and modify itself in terms of differing environmental conditions so that it can best fulfil the purpose and instructions it has received from and within the universal energy.

If we apply this alternative idea to evolution we can immediately see that evolution is not a matter of blind chance or accident or random mutations. What seems random may in fact be driven by the Universalist manifestational drive that is taking a particular organism from its first germ or pre-seed, within implicate Being that has emerged from M-S, out into explicate Existence and form (see Appendix 2). In other words if neo-Darwinist randomness is regarded as operating within the context of metaphysical teleology, then it is seen as functioning within a totally different, purposive view of creation, and far from being here on a Beckettian "dunghill" we are in a purposive Paradise of great beauty which has itself manifested from, and is a reflection of, reality. The materialists, lacking the higher perspective of the soul or universal being, of intuitional contemplation, have failed to sense (unlike the Romantic poets) the drive of the universal energy which pushes into the biological mechanisms they establish and carries them to their teleological goal.

Universalist manifestation may seem not unlike Rupert Sheldrake's formative causation from morphogenetic fields. However, it is different from Sheldrake's view in as much as Sheldrake sees all learning as influencing the subsequent learning of all other animals (or crystals or whatever other forms) of the same kind, a holistic idea that is not necessarily Universalist; whereas Universalist manifestation sees all learning as being parallelled by other forms of the same kind in terms of the metaphysical drive that takes the organism from a seed in Being to its goal in Existence. In other words, Universalism does not need morphogenetic fields which influence learning; it begins with M-S (see Appendix 2) and the breakdown in symmetry which gives rise to the manifestation of particular organisms into self-organising and ascending hierarchical wholes.

On the Universalist manifestational view, Plato is right to be anti-naturalist and essentialist, and his apprehension of an invisible reality behind visible forms is not wrong or false, but a profound insight through his intuitional, contemplative soul which rational materialist theorists have missed. According to manifestational biology, the crux of evolution is that *something is doing it*, something that has entered within biological mechanisms is "doing evolution" to these biological mechanisms in accordance with a manifestational drive and purpose. The biological mechanisms are not purposeless random organisms which have achieved their self-organising by chance.

The Universalist manifestational premiss, then, sees evolution as unfolding through purpose, not chance, as organisms expand through evolution to greater self-organising whole specimens and species just as particles expanded through inflation to greater self-organising stars and galaxies. Moreover, the Universalist manifestational premiss is that the manifestational organism that became an ape is quite distinct from the Universalist manifestational organism that became a human being, so that our philosophical concepts did not evolve by chance from the outlook of apes. On the contrary, the apes have their role in the one whole, which is full of checks and balances, eaters and eaten. Every creature plays a part, has a purpose and is therefore necessary within the whole scheme, and the apes have their place and role, just as humans have their place and role. The emergence of such specimens and creatures, and flora and fauna, as processes of self-organisation to higher wholes represents a continuum of events whose co-existence creates space and whose succession creates time (see Appendix 2).

The same Universalist manifestational context can be applied to the mind-brain problem, to neuroscience's neural Darwinism. The materialists see the brain as functional and consciousness as dependent on the brain, and they reduce mental events to physical bits of brain function. In fact, the brain can be regarded as transmissive, as transmitting consciousness from beyond it, probably through a Bose-Einstein condensate or photons above the brain. On this view the transmitted current of the universal energy or non-local consciousness pours into the brain, perhaps on carrier photons (in contrast to the purer Light which is at the high frequency gamma end of the spectrum). This energy stimulates and drives the neurons, pushes them into interconnectedness and bindings. Thus, the activity of the neurons is a *consequence* of the process of consciousness, not its generator; it traps consciousness and stores it in short-term and long-term memories, but is not itself the producer of consciousness.

Such a view is implicit in New Thought with its focusing on Higher Thought. A number of thinkers have suggested such a view of consciousness, including F.C.S. Schiller in *Riddles of the Sphinx* (1891), William James in *Human Immortality* (1899), Bergson in *L'Energie Spirituelle* (1919) and Jung in his statements of the collective unconscious (1930s). The brain physiologist Peter Fenwick (in conversation with me) and David Lorimer (in *Whole in One*) have also touched on this idea. Roger Sperry's "downward causation" suggests a downward movement of consciousness into the brain, but Sperry's own work bases mind in brain processes and puts him on the side of the functionalist rather than the transmissive view of the brain.

The transmissive view of the brain is to be found throughout Glenn Clark's *The Man who Tapped the Secrets of the Universe*. This is about the ideas of a many-sided American genius Walter Russell, and the following passage is typical: "Can energy tire or become fatigued? Certainly not....The electric energy which motivates us is not within our bodies at all. It is part of the universal supply which flows through us from the Universal Source with an intensity set by our desires and our will." Such a transmissive view of the brain might also explain some of the coincidences in consciousness which I have grouped under the label of synchronicity (page 112, point 6). It is extraordinary, for example, that as I was dictating the beginning of Appendix 2, and was actually talking about "the creation of the universe", the front bell rang and, not too pleased at being disturbed, I opened the door to two lady Jehovah's Witnesses, one of whom said "I can see you're busy, but can I tell you how the universe was created?" (I replied, "I'm just dictating my theory on it now," and, startled, she said "Oh" and they left abashed.)

Universalist manifestation of course opposes the mechanistic approach that sees thoughts as merely neurons which make random connections by accident. It also opposes the mechanistic approach that sees the mind as a computer, just as it opposes neural Darwinism. It sees the functions of consciousness in purposive terms, as driving towards an ascending whole purpose (as I am endeavouring to ascend purposively in these essays), not as a random, chance exercise of the reason as it solves problems (which is how the reason, which sees meaninglessness, is inclined to regard itself). Universalist manifestation thus introduces a new element into the traditional debate between the Creationists and the Evolutionists. In the 19th century the question was: was man created by God or did he evolve as Darwin described? Manifestationists assert that the organism that drove towards the ascending hierarchical whole that has reached its epitome in the minds of our greatest thinkers and artists emerged and manifested from the metaphysical M-S via its more local Being and Existence, and then drove towards its goal with teleological purpose, not by random chance.

What evidence is there for the Universalist manifestational view of evolution, and the transmissive view of the brain? Materialists are quick to scoff and say "None": "Metaphysical nay-sayers such as Plato can't produce any evidence." Evidence for manifestation-transmission must be high on the agenda of a metaphysical science programme. Until technology permits us to locate the high frequency manifestation of the Fire or Light, which mystics have approached intuitively, as the reality in the microworld which Einstein and Bohm have sought, the new science will have to observe evolution and brain function as consequences of transmissions of the Fire or Light. In this connection universal studies like my own *The Fire and the Stones* will be relevant, together with studies relating to particular cultures such as Mohammad Mokri's *La Lumière et le Feu dans l'Iran Ancien et leur Démythification en Islam*. While the evidence is produced, and it *is* capable of being produced and of being tested, it must be re-emphasised that there is very little evidence for materialistic evolution and for neural Darwinism. The materialistic and metaphysical approaches to evolution and consciousness are rival theories which both need to be tested and investigated in equal measure.

The materialistic view holds sway at Cambridge. At any conference on the sciences and philosophy at Oxford or Cambridge, reductionists and materialists will outnumber metaphysicals by ten to one. That does not mean that the ten are right; only that their rational approach is in the majority.

Many incorrect assumptions are made, including the idea that there can be no general principles about the universe because when it inflated it split into compartments like bubbles in foam; and that our invisible universe is merely a bubble with laws that may be quite different from our neighbouring universes. John Barrow holds this view, but how can he know? He has not been beyond our visible universe, he does not know, he has only a conjecture. And in making it has he not created a general principle: that there are no general principles in the universe?

The feeling is growing among those seeking a truly whole vision which accommodates all layers of man, that the materialists and neo-Darwinists and neuroscientists have perpetrated an intellectual swindle, that in reducing mental states to physical states they have "faked" a materialist mind and come to believe in their own fake. Two giants stood up to materialism in their time. Coleridge endeavoured to reconcile physics and metaphysics in his prose writings, and opposed Hartleyan associationism on the grounds that materialism encouraged the mind to be dead and lazy rather than vital: "Newton was a mere materialist - *Mind* in his system is always passive - a lazy looker-on on an external World....Any system built on the passiveness of the mind must be false as a system" (*Collected Letters* II, p709). And T.S. Eliot's *Four Quartets* attempt a whole vision, drawing on Indian philosophy and several disciplines in approaching reality. Neither Coleridge nor Eliot would have swallowed neo-Darwinism or neural-Darwinism, and the symbols their consciousnesses channelled reflected a metaphysical

Jungian order as well as a neural order. D.H. Lawrence said of heliocentrism, indicating his solar plexus, "I don't feel it *here*." Many now feel in their heart of hearts that the symbolic consciousness of Coleridge and Eliot cannot be reduced to the chance mental development of a neural ape.

Neuroscience has made discoveries through the overlapping of disciplines. Metaphysical science is making corresponding discoveries. Most discoveries are made in areas where disciplines overlap; I think immediately of Crick's biochemistry and DNA, and (on the other side) Coleridge's German metaphysics and psychological imagination, which became the Romantic movement. It is my contention that if neuroscience is seen within the context of metaphysical science, with its manifestational view of evolution and its view of the brain as transmissive, then further discoveries are possible, together with a new reconciliation of superficially opposed and warring outlooks. Is it too much to hope that manifestational neo-Darwinists and transmissive neuroscientists will join the Metaphysical Revolution in the coming decade and echo the new metaphysical understanding of the universe and reality, and of the new science and philosophy, that I have outlined in these essays?

Notes for Appendix 1-3

1. I have deliberately left mysticism out of the Form from Movement theory. It is, however, worth noting that mystics who have seen the metaphysical Fire or Light claim that they have perceived the first principle of infinite movement at some point in the course of the manifestational process, through an eternal and infinite part of their consciousness. Mystics sometimes say that they perceive this infinite movement as a stillness, although the energy of the Fire or Light which enters their beings could not enter them dynamically from a stillness. The apparent stillness of the infinite movement is like the apparent stillness of the physical sun, which is of course a continuous movement although it is perceived as a stillness.

2. Patricia Churchland, *Neurophilosophy*, p242.

3. Gerald Edelman, *Bright Air, Brilliant Fire*, p239.

BIBLIOGRAPHY

ADAMS, Brooks, *The Law of Civilisation and Decay*, Vintage, New York, 1955.

BARROW, John, *Theories of Everything*, Oxford University Press, U.K., 1991.

BERGSON, Henri (-Louis), *Introduction to Metaphysics*, 1903.

— *L'Energie Spirituelle*, Presses Universitaires de France, Paris, 1919.

BOHM, David, *A Suggested Interpretation of the Quantum Theory of "Hidden" Variables*, Physical Review, volume 85, number 2, January 15th 1952.

— *Wholeness and the Implicate Order*, Routledge, London, 1980.

BUCKE, Richard Maurice, *Cosmic Consciousness*, Citadel Press, U.S.A., 1989.

CASTILLEJO, David, *The Expanding Force in Newton's Cosmos*, Ediciones de Arte Y Bibliofilia, Madrid, 1981.

CHURCHLAND, Patricia, *Neurophilosophy: Toward a Unified Science of the Mind/Brain*, MIT Press, U.S.A., 1986.

CLARK, Glenn, *The Man who Tapped the Secrets of the Universe*, The University of Science and Philosophy, U.S.A., 1946/1989.

COLERIDGE, Samuel Taylor, *Collected Letters*, ed. by Earl Leslie Griggs, 6 vols, 1956-71.

DAVIES, Paul, *The Matter Myth*, Viking, U.K., 1991.

— *The Mind of God*, Simon and Schuster, U.K., 1992.

DAWKINS, Richard, *The Blind Watchmaker*, Penguin, U.K., 1986/1991.

EDELMAN, Gerald, *Bright Air, Brilliant Fire: On the Matter of the Mind*, Allen Lane, The Penguin Press, U.K., 1992.

FOX, Matthew, *Illuminations of Hildegard of Bingen*, Bear and Co., U.S.A., 1985.

FUKUYAMA, Francis, *The End of History and the Last Man*, Hamish Hamilton, London, 1992.

GIBBON, Edward, *Decline and Fall of the Roman Empire*, one-volume abridgement by D.M. Low, Penguin, London, 1963.

GOULD, Stephen Jay, *Wonderful Life*, Hutchinson Radius, U.K., 1990.

GUENON, René, *The Multiple States of Being*, Larson, U.S.A., 1984.

HAGGER, Nicholas, *The Fire and the Stones: A Grand Unfied Theory of World History and Religion*, Element, U.K., 1991.

— *Selected Poems: A Metaphysical's Way of Fire*, Element, U.K., 1991.

HARMAN, Willis, *Global Mind Change*, Institute of Noetic Sciences, U.S.A., 1988.

— *Metaphysics, The Union Whose Time Has Come*, Noetic Sciences Review, Winter 1990/1.

— *A Re-examination of the Metaphysical Foundations of Modern Science*, Institute of Noetic Sciences, U.S.A., 1991.

HAWKING, Stephen, *A Brief History of Time*, Bantam Press, U.K., 1990.

HEIDEGGER, Martin, *Being and Time*, Basil Blackwell, U.K., 1990.

HUXLEY, Aldous, *The Perennial Philosophy*, Collins, Fontana, U.K., 1959.

JAMES, William, *The Varieties of Religious Experience*, Collins, Fontana, U.K., 1960.

— *Human Immortality*, Constable, U.K., 1899.

JASPERS, Karl, *Existenzphilosophie*, 1938.

KENNEDY, Paul, *The Rise and Fall of the Great Powers*, Unwin Hyman, London, 1988.

KERMODE, Frank, *Romantic Image*, Routledge, U.K., 1957.

KUHN, Thomas, *The Structure of Scientific Revolutions*, University of Chicago Press, U.S.A., 1970.

LIBERMAN, Jacob, *Light, Medicine of the Future*, Bear & Co., U.S.A., 1991.

LORIMER, David, *Whole in One*, Arkana, U.K., 1990.

MARCEL, Gabriel, *A Metaphysical Journal (1913-23)*, Paris, 1927.

McNEILL, William, *The Rise of the West*, University of Chicago Press, U.S.A., 1963.

MILTON, Richard, *The Facts of Life: Shattering the Myth of Darwinism*, Sinclair-Stevenson, U.K., 1992.

MOKRI, Mohammad, *La Lumière et le Feu dans L'Iran Ancien et leur Démythification en Islam*, Éditions Peeters, Leuven, 1982.

MOTT, N.F., *Elements of Wave Mechanics*, Cambridge University Press, U.K., 1962.

ROSE, Steven, *The Making of Memory*, Bantam, U.K., 1992.

SANFORD, Agnes, *The Healing Light*, Arthur James, U.K., 1972.

SARTRE, Jean-Paul, *Being and Nothingness*, Methuen, U.K., 1957.

SCHILLER, F.C.S., *Riddles of the #*, Swan Sonnnenschein, U.K., 1891.

SCHNAPPER, Edith, *The Spiral Path of Spiritual Psychology*, C.W. Danial, U.K., 1985.

SECRET OF THE GOLDEN FLOWER, THE, trans, by Richard Wilhelm, Harcourt, Brace and World, New York, 1962.

SHELDRAKE, Rupert, *A New Science of Life*, Granada, U.K., 1988.

SMUTS, Jan, *Holism and Evolution*, Macmillan, New York, 1926.

SPENGLER, Oswald, *The Decline of the West*, George Allen and Unwin, U.K., 1959.

SPERRY, Roger, *Structure and Significance of the Consciousness Revolution*, The Journal of Mind and Behaviour, Vol 8. No 1, U.S.A., Winter 1987.

TOYNBEE, Arnold, *A Study of History*, Oxford University Press, 12 vols., U.K., 1934, 1939, 1954, 1961.

UNDERHILL, Evelyn, *Mysticism*, Methuen, U.K., 1960.

WEBER, Renée, (ed), *Dialogues with Scientists and Sages: The Search for Unity*, Routledge, U.K., 1986.

WHITE, John, *Kundalini, Evolution and Enlightenment*, Paragon House, New York, 1990.

WHITEHEAD, Alfred North, *Process and Reality, Science and the Modern World* and *Modes of Thought*, in *Whitehead, an Anthology*, sel. by Northrop and Gross, Cambridge University Press, London, 1953.

— *An Introduction to Mathematics*, Oxford University Press, U.K., 1958.

WILBER, Ken, *Eye to Eye*, Shambhala, U.S.A., 1990.

WILLIAMSON, J.J., *The Structure of All*, The Society of Metaphysicians Ltd., U.K., 1970.

WILSON, Edmund, *Axel's Castle*, Charles Scribner's Sons, U.S.A., 1959.

ZOHAR, Danah, *The Quantum Self*, Bloomsbury, U.K., 1990.

ZUKAV, Gary, *The Seat of the Soul*, Rider, U.K., 1990.